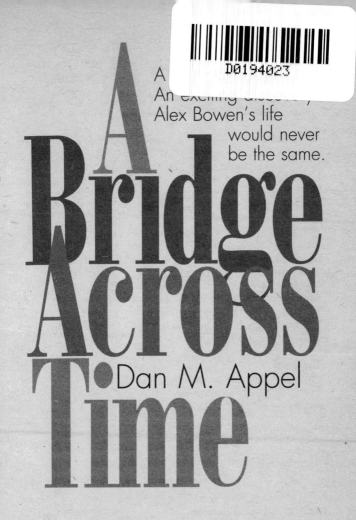

A
An exciting discovery,
Alex Bowen's life
would never
be the same.

A Bridge Across Time

Dan M. Appel

REVIEW AND HERALD® PUBLISHING ASSOCIATION
HAGERSTOWN, MD 21740

Texts credited to NEB are from *The New English Bible*.
© The Delegates of the Oxford University Press and the
Syndics of the Cambridge University Press 1961, 1970.
Reprinted by permission.

Texts credited to NIV are from the *Holy Bible, New
International Version*. Copyright © 1973, 1978, 1984,
International Bible Society. Used by permission of
Zondervan Bible Publishers.

Bible texts credited to RSV are from the Revised
Standard Version of the Bible, copyright © 1946, 1952,
1971, by the Division of Christian Education of the
National Council of the Churches of Christ in the U.S.A.
Used by permission.

This book was
Edited by Rebecca Lane
Cover design by Helcio Deslandes
Typeset: 11/12.5 Palatino

PRINTED IN U.S.A.

00 99 98 97 96   5 4 3 2 1

R&H Cataloging Service
Appel, Dan M.
    A bridge across time

    1. Sabbath.
                263.1

ISBN 0-8280-1049-8

DEDICATION

To my parents, Mel and June,
who lived the ideas
written about in this book in such a positive
way that I adopted them as my own and dedi-
cated my life to sharing them with others.

ACKNOWLEDGMENTS

THANKS TO:

Cecil Murphy, who mentored me in my first pastorate and encouraged me to write.

Jan Haluska, who took time out of his very busy schedule to give me constructive criticism and suggestions.

Ken Cox, who encouraged me to submit this manuscript for publication.

Lori Aab and Jane Weber, who read and encouraged and corrected.

Charla, Danny, and David, my wonderful family, who endured innumerable rough drafts, sacrificed time with me, and encouraged me to write.

All the men and women down through the ages who experienced the gift of God's time and passed the knowledge of that incredible gift down to all who are desiring a deeper and richer relationship with God today.

CHAPTER 1

"That has to be the dumbest, most idiotic, far-fetched, legalistic claptrap I've ever heard of!" Alex Bowen spat the words through clenched teeth.

Screech. He pounded the brakes. Another red light.

He sat at the stoplight fuming, his fingers lashing the steering wheel like an angry cat's tail. His day at the office had been frustrating enough. And now this traffic. Every slow driver in town had chosen the same moment to head for home.

"Doesn't anyone take driver's ed anymore?" he muttered.

The day had started badly and gone downhill from there. And then Clark Hanson had wandered into Alex's office an hour before quitting time with his crazy request. It was a fitting end for a horrible Thursday.

"Why on earth is this planet inhabited with such obstinate fools?" Alex asked himself. "And why do they all have to work for me?" It wasn't fair, especially now when he desperately needed a good draftsman on the payroll.

The traffic light flashed green. Alex stomped the accelerator and kept mumbling. "Is it too much to ask that my employees conform to some kind of reasonable workweek? What makes one guy think he's so special?"

Alex had founded Bowen and Associates 10 years before. Now they had grown into one of the largest, most aggressive architectural engineering firms in Georgia. He was proud of their track record. They had a reputation for getting the job done, even if it took weekends and long nights to finish. Alex hated missing deadlines.

True, the schedule exhausted his employees and left little time for his family. But he never demanded anything that he wasn't willing to do himself.

Alex knew how to work. Years ago he had boarded a bus and ridden away from his home in little Ellijay, Georgia. Back then he had nothing. Nothing except firsthand knowledge of hard work. Nineteen years on the back end of his daddy's mules taught him that.

While growing up he spent his summers working from first light until it was too dark to see a furrow in the cornfield. Winter meant chores, school, more chores, and then schoolwork. Kids in Gilmer County grew up believing they could do anything if they put their minds to it. And Alex had.

That's what upset him today. Why couldn't everyone have the same dedication to getting a job done? He'd lost his best draftsman a month before, and the extra work meant long hours of overtime for everyone. This week he'd hired the ideal man to fill the opening. At least, the guy seemed ideal at first. And then this happened.

Wheeling into his driveway, he stopped the

car and thought for a minute. Why, of all times, must he deal with a distraction like this? Just when he'd signed the contract to engineer the twin towers for Bill Eckroth.

Marching into the house, he tossed his windbreaker into the front closet and stomped toward the kitchen to find his wife.

"You look cheerful tonight," Melanie greeted as she turned a steak on the kitchen grill.

"Sorry, Mel. It's been a bad day." Alex shook his head. "Where are the kids?"

"Out back setting the picnic table. They decided they wanted to have one more picnic before fall sets in," Melanie said, nodding toward the back door. "Would you take the salad out? I'll bring the steaks and we'll be ready to eat."

"Sure thing!" Alex reached across the counter and gave her a kiss. "Sorry I'm such a grouch. Boy, those steaks smell great!"

"Thank you, sir," Melanie smiled. "Now if you'll get out of my kitchen and have a seat at the table, you might find out that they taste good, too. I marinated them in Schillo's special sauce."

"All right, I'm outta here," Alex laughed and picked up the salad bowl. "Anything else I can carry?"

"Nope, just your appetite. Now git!"

❦

"You know, Melanie, I've got a real problem," Alex told his wife as they washed dishes after supper that night. "I think I told you about

Clark Hanson, the new draftsman I hired on Monday. He's the best I've ever had. He's quick, he's precise, and he knows computer design like he invented it. Whoever trained him did a fantastic job, and Clark must have had plenty of talent to begin with."

Alex reached behind Melanie's back and swiped a chocolate-chip cookie from the big cookie jar.

"There's something else," Alex added. "He's just a nice guy. Bill Eckroth called the other day, mad about something as usual. Clark happened to take the call."

"Poor guy," Melanie commented. "Bill's mouth is pretty bad even when he's not mad."

"Yeah, but Clark just ignored it and treated him as though he was our most important customer. Later I ran into Bill at city council. He couldn't say enough about Clark."

"That's a first!" Melanie pulled a gallon of milk from the refrigerator, filled a glass, and handed it to Alex. "Have something healthy with those cookies," she winked.

Alex dunked his cookie and put the glass down again. "Everyone likes the guy, Mel. I don't even have to worry about customers overhearing when he tells jokes—they're usually funny, but clean enough to tell your grandmother."

"So what's the matter?" Melanie asked.

"I may have to let him go."

"But you need him!" Melanie exclaimed. She stretched to set her mixing bowl in its place above the cupboard. "I'll never get to see you if you keep doing so much overtime. What's this guy done?"

"Nothing! It's what he wants to do." Alex picked up the towel and started drying a yellow pitcher. "He comes into my office just before quitting time and asks for this Saturday off. He wants all his Saturdays off!"

"Maybe he has some kind of family problem."

"No, but get this. He says he goes to church on what he calls 'Sabbath.' According to him, the Bible says to work six days and rest on the seventh."

"Doesn't he realize he'll put the whole office behind schedule?" Melanie asked.

"That's not the problem." Alex finished drying the last of the dishes and tugged the red apron over his head. "He's willing to work Sundays to make up the work. In fact, it sounds like he could use the money. He says he'll be glad to work whenever he can."

"There you go, problem solved," Melanie declared.

"But Mel, if I make everyone else come in, I can't let him off. Even worse, he's brand-new. If I let him take the day, everyone will say I'm playing favorites. I've met some fanatics in my life, but this guy takes the cake!"

"Didn't he mention this on his application?" Melanie questioned.

"Yeah, but I guess I overlooked it. He apologized for not saying something sooner this week. He said he just wanted a chance to prove himself first."

"And has he done that?"

"Sure has. We caught up on a month of work this week."

Melanie frowned as she wiped the sink and hung up the towel. "You don't have to keep him if you don't want to. He's still on probation. And if you do keep him, that's your business, isn't it? As long as he works Sundays, why should anyone else complain?"

She flipped off the kitchen light and followed Alex into the living room. "But something else bothers me," she said.

"What's that?" Alex sighed, kicked off his shoes, and leaned back on the couch.

"Alex, you're a Sunday school teacher. Your daddy was a Sunday school teacher. You know your Bible. Why didn't you just show him that Saturday's the wrong day to worship on?"

"I tried. I said something about Sunday being my Sabbath. He smiled and said he understood, but then he added that Saturday is God's Sabbath according to the Bible."

"It's in the Bible?"

"Yeah, I thought he was nuts. I asked him where in the Bible. He quoted Exodus 20:10, where it says, 'The seventh day is the sabbath of the Lord thy God.' He nodded toward my calendar and said the only day God asks us to worship on is Saturday, the seventh day. He says the

Bible Sabbath begins at sunset on Friday and ends at sunset the next evening."

"Where does it say that?"

"In Leviticus 23:32. I asked him."

"How'd you answer him?"

"What could I say?" Alex shrugged. "We didn't have much time. I told him there's plenty of proof that Sunday is the right day to go to church. I'll show it to him on Monday."

"So you're going to keep him on?" Melanie's eyes twinkled.

"At least for now. I don't have a choice if I'm going to get Eckroth's job done. But I've got to change some of his ideas. I told him it's ridiculous to say the whole Christian world is wrong about the day of worship. He just gave me that same grin and said he'd be glad to read any Bible texts I could show him."

"Sounds like you've got your work cut out for you."

"It shouldn't take much to prove him wrong. Want to help?"

"Sure. But I'm going to Ali's baby shower, so you're on your own for a while. I'll be back by 9:00 tonight," she promised.

Alex sat thoughtfully on the couch after Melanie left. He recalled all the traditions his family had passed down to him. His mouth watered at the memory of his mother's fried chicken, pickled okra, and her sweet potato pie.

He smiled as he remembered swimming in the creek with his brothers. And he thought about going to church every Sunday, his family lined up in their pew like eight blackbirds on a wire.

The Bowens had lived in north Georgia for almost 200 years—in the same community, on the same road, in the same cove. Before that, they'd lived in the same county in Scotland, on the same road, on a highland plateau for hundreds of years. They could have been there since the Celts settled the land, for all Alex knew.

Yes, change was hard for his family. Maybe even impossible, unless there was a mighty good reason for it. And no good reason existed for throwing out his ancestors' day of worship. They'd kept Sunday for centuries before the British evicted them to the New World.

And they all stood by the Bible, the Good Book, as Alex's dad had called it. "That's a book to be read and lived by," the old man always told his children.

So Alex knew that the Bible held the answer to his dilemma. The only way to find truth was to dig in and study it out for himself. Solutions would appear in their own good time. Too many people took the word of every fly-by-night preacher or guru who could purchase television time.

Striding into the den, he pulled *Strong's Concordance* from the shelf. The giant book, listing every word in the Bible, had always helped him out. Whenever his Sunday school students brought questions about the Bible, Alex encour-aged them to search for themselves with just a Bible and concordance.

Now he needed to do his own search. Placing the concordance, his Bible, a yellow legal pad, and a cup of coffee on the kitchen table, he settled down to begin.

Two hours later Alex threw down his gold Cross pen in disgust. First he'd tried looking up "Sunday." Apparently the word wasn't in the Bible. Then Melanie joined him and suggested that he try "first." After all, Sunday is the first day of the week.

"I remember my grandma saying something about that," she told Alex. "Every Sunday morning when I was little, Grams used to say, 'Melanie Ann, the Bible says don't forget to as-semble yourselves together for worship on the first day of the week. So put down the funnies and get ready!'"

Unfortunately, Alex and Melanie couldn't find that text, either—the closest one was Hebrews 10:25, but it didn't say anything about the first day of the week. They were stumped.

"Well," Alex said, "what now?"

❧

Next morning at work Alex motioned one of his engineers, Scorp Johnson, into his office. Scorp often volunteered as a lay preacher and knew his Bible well. Closing the door, Alex asked, "Where in the Bible does it say we're supposed to worship on Sunday?"

"What?" Scorp laughed.

"Where does the Bible tell us to worship on Sunday? I was talking with the new draftsman the other day, and he asked for Saturdays off so he could go to church. He says he's Christian, not Jewish. He thinks God tells us in the Bible that He set Saturday aside for worship. Sabbath, he calls it. Got any ideas for setting him straight?"

"Sure. I've got some books at home you can use. I'll pick 'em up on my lunch hour for you."

"Thanks, I owe you one," Alex said later when Scorp dropped off the books. "Wish me luck!"

"No problem. He doesn't have a leg to stand on."

Driving home that night, Alex opened the windows and savored the earthy smells of autumn. *Fall is a feast for the senses,* he thought as one flaming tree after another flashed by. He sniffed the pungent aroma of hickory and ripe catawba. *I'm sure glad God created the seasons the way He did,* he mused.

That evening, after building a fire in the fireplace, he sat down with Melanie to read Scorp's books. Soon they had three pages of ammunition written on the yellow pad. Sunday morning they studied again before Sunday school. Then, to make sure they had all their bases covered, they invited the pastor and his family home for lunch and spent the afternoon gathering more information.

Before going to bed that night, they condensed their study into 10 points:

1. The seventh-day Sabbath was given to the Jews only. It was to be a weekly celebration of their deliverance from Egypt. It had not been kept by God's people before Mount Sinai.

2. Jesus abolished the observance of the seventh-day Sabbath at the cross. From that time on, He and the early Christians worshiped on Sunday in honor of the Resurrection.

3. The resurrection of Jesus from the dead is the greatest event in human history—greater, even, than the creation of the world. Therefore, honoring the Resurrection takes precedence over any celebration honoring Creation.

4. As Christians we are not under the old covenant, the Ten Commandments, but under grace and the new covenant.

5. God instituted the Sabbath to guarantee that His people would take one day to focus on Him and their relationship with Him. He blessed the act of worship, not one particular day. The spirit in which the day is kept is more important. We choose to worship on Sunday because most of the Christian world has set that day aside.

6. Those who worship on Saturday can't really know that it's the correct day. In the thousands of years since Creation, time records have been lost, and the calendar has been changed.

7. Since we live on a round planet, it's impossible for the whole world to keep the same

day. Times are different around the world; therefore, keeping the Sabbath is impossible.

8. If Sunday is the wrong day for worship, why hasn't somebody figured it out before this? Why don't the great religious leaders and pastors of all churches make an issue of it?

9. If worshiping on Sunday is wrong, God's Spirit would make us sensitive to the fact. Since He hasn't, it must be OK.

10. If we were to keep the seventh-day Sabbath instead of Sunday, we'd be out of step with the world. We'd be ridiculed, and we'd have a hard time doing business. Holding a job would be next to impossible. Finally, our credibility as Christians would be destroyed. People would think we were part of a cult.

"Well, if that doesn't convince him, nothing will," Alex muttered as he turned out the light. "There's enough evidence there to convince a jury!"

"Alex!" Melanie bolted up in bed. "Turn on the light. I just thought of something! Sunday *is* the seventh day of the week. Clark's got his days mixed up."

"Hold on," Alex held up his hand. "If we say that, we shoot ourselves in the foot, Mel. Our second argument says that Jesus changed the day of worship from the seventh day to the first day. If we say Sunday's the seventh day, that means we should be worshiping on Monday. Besides, Saturday's always the seventh day on the calendar."

"I guess you're right. Alex, are you sure you can remember all the texts that go with the arguments?"

"Yes, Mel." Alex rolled over and laughed. "I marked them in my Bible. Now, give me a kiss and go to sleep so we don't have to worry all night."

CHAPTER 2

"Hey, hon, how was your day?" Clark breezed into the kitchen and gave Connie a hug.

Bending down, he picked little Emily up off the floor, and swung her overhead. With the laughing girl under one arm, he turned into the living room to find their boys, Shane and Eric. He said nothing about work.

Happy giggles floated from the living room. Connie smiled, remembering how much Clark had changed since she first met him. He was the typical macho construction worker when they married a few years after high school.

Back then Clark didn't rush home to give his kids piggyback rides. Usually he didn't even eat supper with them. On Monday nights he always headed for Rocky's Sports Bar. He stayed for hours, downing beers with the guys, watching football, telling jokes. Tuesdays meant grabbing a few cold ones with his Army buddies. Next came bowling on Wednesdays and the weekly meeting of the Hamilton County Mustang Club on Thursdays.

And then Fridays. "Connie, you know I need to unwind with the guys," he'd explain on his way out the door. "I'll take the kids to the zoo tomorrow. Promise!" Then he'd kiss her and jump in the car. The tomorrows he promised for the kids never seemed to come.

Connie considered divorce a few times, and

once she went as far as the lawyer's office to sign the papers. But then she couldn't do it. Clark held a job, provided a good living, and hadn't cheated on her as far as she knew. Some of her friends didn't have it that good.

Still, she couldn't really call their relationship a marriage; it was just a convenient living arrangement. Clark kept a roof over their heads while she kept the clothes washed and the floors clean. And she put supper on the table whenever he decided he wanted to eat at home.

Then things changed. One day at work Clark met a Christian man named Perry Davis. As the two men became friends, Clark noticed the joy in Perry's life. Eventually Clark accepted Jesus Christ as his own Saviour.

Clark still spent time with his friends, but he quit drinking. Then he threw away his cigarettes. Their marriage became what Connie had always dreamed it would be, and time with the kids became Clark's priority. They joined a church and attended together every week. At last they became a family that played together and prayed together.

Connie even noticed changes in their physical relationship. People said they acted like newlyweds. The guys on the job teased Clark about the notes in his lunch pail that left him smiling and sometimes blushing.

Later another Christian friend introduced them to an idea that enriched their lives even more.

"You what?" Clark exclaimed when Dwight Hendershot first told them he went to church on Saturday. "Christians go to church on Sunday." But as they listened to Dwight's explanation, both Clark and Connie grew more fascinated.

They discovered that God made the seventh day of the week special when He created the world. "It's called the Sabbath," Dwight explained. "It's like a gift of quality time He's given each of us. Time with God, time with family."

Dwight continued, "See, God created us to be friends with Him. He enjoys us just like a loving father enjoys his children. The Sabbath gives us time to focus on that relationship."

"Shouldn't we be Christians seven days a week?" Clark asked.

"Sure, and imagine how much better your whole week would be if you put aside all your work and spent 24 hours just enjoying God and each other. Give it a try."

Clark and Connie were deeply moved. They studied about the Sabbath in the Bible, and eventually they did give it a try. Before long, the Sabbath became the most fantastic part of their week. "How did we ever survive without this time?" Clark often asked.

Our life is so different now, mused Connie, *and I wouldn't change it for anything!* Still, she wondered what had happened with Clark's job.

The thick soup bubbled on the stove. Arranging crackers and bowls on the table, she called her family for supper.

"Well," she said after Clark asked God's blessing on the meal, "what happened? Are you going to keep us in suspense all night?"

Clark laughed. "It's been an amazing day, Connie. I don't quite know where to begin. You know how we prayed this morning and asked God to guide my conversation with Alex?"

She nodded and started ladling hot soup into Clark's bowl.

"Well, I felt tempted to skirt the issue of the Sabbath. Even if I won an argument with him, I'd lose my job and a guy I'd like for a friend. I wanted to share what we've discovered without turning him off and preaching at him." Clark took a deep breath and looked at his wife. "You know, I was really scared. I spent a lot of time praying before I talked to him."

"And?"

"And," Clark grinned again, "I still have the job."

"Clark, that's fantastic!" Connie leaped from her chair, wrapped her arms around his neck, and kissed him. "I knew God would help you. I just knew it. Oh, Clark, isn't God good?"

"Now, hold on," Clark laughed. "I don't know how long it will last, but at least I'm employed for the week. Alex is buried under projects he's doing for Kozlicki and Eckroth, so he needs my help. I guess we'll just have to play it a day at a time."

Connie slid onto her husband's lap and hugged him again. "Clark Hanson, I'm so proud of you!" she whispered into his ear. "I knew it was going to work out."

"Mommy, what's happening? Tell us, too!"

Connie and Clark turned and looked at the confused faces of Eric, Shane, and Emily. The children waited impatiently to hear the news.

"Daddy's new job is going really well. So I'm just happy and very proud."

Shane tilted his head and wrinkled his forehead. "Then why are you crying and laughing at the same time?" he asked.

"Because Mommy's really, really happy," she explained.

"Now tell us what happened," Connie begged, returning to her own chair. Clark's mysterious grin only made her more impatient to dig the words out.

"Well, Alex asked me to have lunch with him. So we're sitting there, and he pulls out a yellow sheet covered with notes. He'd made a list of 10 statements about Sabbath and Sunday. Here," Clark fished in his pocket and brought out a folded piece of yellow legal paper, "I brought it home so you could read it."

Connie reached for the list, and Clark added, "I'll tell you something, Connie. Alex may have grown up in the backwoods, but he sure got an education somewhere! He's sharp as a new knife. You should see his Bible. It's about worn out."

"What did he say?" Connie asked.

"Well, Alex looked me square in the eye with those eyes of his that seem to go right through you. Then he asked, 'Just why does this Sabbath business mean so much to you? It's all new to me, and I'm curious.'"

Connie looked thoughtful. "You know, it sounds like he really does want to be fair with you. What did you tell him?"

"I asked him to look at the first three chapters of Genesis with me. Remember what we thought when Dwight first told us about going to church on Saturday?"

"Sure, we thought it sounded downright weird."

"Exactly. But when we took an open look at it in the Bible, it really made sense. It clicked for me when I read the Creation story in Genesis, so that's where I started with Alex."

Clark still hadn't touched his soup. Pushing it aside, he continued his story for Connie. "In Genesis 1 we reviewed the Creation story together. We really have a lot of common ground. He believes God created the world in seven days, just as we do. Then we read what happened on the seventh day of Creation—how God rested on that day and sanctified it, or set it apart for a holy purpose. Alex said he thought this Sabbath was meant only for the Jews, not Christians."

"But the Jewish nation didn't even exist yet," Connie protested.

"True, and I reminded him about that. I told him how God created the Sabbath for all humans before sin even entered the world. Then we turned to Mark 2:27, where it says that God gave the Sabbath as a gift for humanity. I don't think he'd ever read the text in that context before.

"What really intrigued him, though, was how the devil feels about the Sabbath. I shared with him how God gave men and women three gifts at Creation. First, He gave us life itself. Then there's the family, where we discover what love is all about. And finally the Sabbath, a gift of quality time when we set aside our work to focus on God and each other. I reminded him how God's enemy has attacked and tried to destroy each of these gifts—life, the family, and our time with God."

"And was he still following you after all that?" Connie asked.

"Yeah, he was really patient. Finally, we turned to Isaiah 58—you know, the verse about turning your feet . . ."

"Oh, I love that one." Connie grabbed the Bible off the shelf and leafed through it quickly. "Here it is. Let's see, verse 14 says, 'If you keep your feet from breaking the Sabbath and from doing as you please on my holy day, if you call the Sabbath a delight and the Lord's holy day honorable, and if you honor it by not going your own way and not doing as you please or speaking idle words, then you will find your joy in the Lord, and I will cause you to ride on the heights of the land and to feast on the heritance of your father Jacob. The mouth of the Lord has spoken.'

"Mmm," grunted Clark. "That's the one. So when . . ."

"I think that's one of my favorite places in the whole Bible," Connie interrupted. "I love how God says that honoring the Sabbath will open the door for a delightful relationship with Him. I think that's the most important key to a successful Christian life, next to accepting Jesus' sacrifice on the cross. Remember when we first started keeping the Sabbath, Clark? It was like a whole new dimension opened up in our relationship with God."

"Well, when Alex read Isaiah 58, he just harrumphed," Clark said, "and then he reached over and crossed out the first statement on that yellow pad. He said, 'I suppose that if God made the seventh day holy at Creation, we have to assume that Enoch and Noah and Job all worshiped on that day, too. At least, we don't have any evidence to the contrary.'"

"'That's true,' I told him. Then we talked about how the Sabbath was important to God long before the children of Israel became a nation. Remember when God gave the Israelites manna to eat in the desert? They weren't supposed to gather manna on Sabbath. We looked up the story in Exodus 16. I pointed out that all this happened *before* the Israelites were given the law on tables of stone at Mount Sinai."

Connie looked thoughtful. "Do you think Alex has ever heard about any of this before?"

"I doubt it," Clark replied, "because he scribbled notes about everything on his legal pad. Then he put down his pen and asked about the second statement on his list."

"Daddy, can we eat now?"

Shocked, Clark glanced at little Emily. Then he turned to the two boys. All three children waited quietly. Connie gasped when she realized she hadn't filled their soup bowls.

Clark laughed. "I'm sorry, Punkin. Daddy and Mom got so busy talking, we almost forgot about supper." The kids giggled, and Clark shook his head, surprised that the hungry youngsters had waited so long.

After supper Clark leaned back in his old leather recliner and sighed. He loved the relaxing feel of cool leather after a hard day. *Man, I'm glad we spent the money for good quality when we had it,* he thought, *because we sure couldn't afford it now.* Closing his eyes, he listened to the rain as it tapped on the window.

❦

"Clark, feel like a mug of herb tea?"

Shaking his head no, he looked up at Connie. Then he nodded.

"Yeah, on second thought, I believe I will have one. Are the kids already in bed?"

"A half hour ago. You were spaced out, and I figured they could survive one night without a story from their dad."

"Sorry, Con; I was just remembering a previous boss's reaction when I said I wanted Saturdays off."

"That's history, Clark. Let's worry about today." She smiled and handed him a big blue mug of licorice tea.

"Now," Connie reminded him, "you were going to tell me what Alex said about the Sabbath being abolished at the cross."

"I think Alex was really counting on that idea to show me the error of my ways," Clark began. "Everything else was just there to bolster his arguments."

"How did he react?"

Clark sighed. "I'm afraid I wasn't as tactful as I should have been, Connie. I asked him to produce even one text of Scripture showing that Jesus had abolished the seventh day as a day of worship."

Clark reached for his Bible on the coffee table and pulled out his wrinkled study notes on the Sabbath. "First, I told him to look up John 1 and Colossians 1:15-18. Those verses say Jesus created the world. That means He's the one who created the Sabbath and made it holy, so He's the only one who can change it. Surely, if He changed something so fundamental to the Christian life, it would have been pretty dramatic, and at least one of the Gospel writers would have recorded the change. But not one of them says a single word about it!"

"Whew," Connie breathed. "That wasn't a very nice way to say that, Clark. Couldn't you have been a little more tactful?"

"Yeah, but it didn't seem to faze him. He was

really gracious and just kept going. He asked, 'Doesn't Colossians 2:13-17 say that all of the Old Testament laws were done away with?' "

Clark flipped through his Bible to the passage. "So I asked what he meant by that. Then Alex read me this: 'God made you alive with Christ. He forgave us all our sins, having canceled the written code, with its regulations, that was against us and that stood opposed to us; he took it away, nailing it to the cross. And having disarmed the powers and authorities, he made a public spectacle of them, triumphing over them by the cross. Therefore do not let anyone judge you by what you eat or drink, or with regard to a religious festival, a New Moon celebration or a Sabbath day. These are a shadow of the things that were to come; the reality, however is found in Christ' " (NIV).

Connie watched as Clark turned to another text. He continued, "Then Alex read Ephesians 2:14, 15, which says that 'He himself is our peace, who has made the two one and has destroyed the barrier, the dividing wall of hostility, by abolishing in his flesh the law with its commandments and regulations' [NIV].

"Then Alex just closed his Bible. 'There you go,' he told me. 'I don't think you're going to find it stated any plainer than that!'"

"So?" Connie motioned with her arms. "Did you tell him what we learned about the laws?"

"Yeah, I asked him if he had ever studied the difference between the kinds of law in the Bible.

He said yes. Once he'd even invited a rabbi to talk to his Sunday school class. I told him, 'So you know that the Bible talks about different kinds of law—civil laws, like our traffic laws, and laws concerning murder and property rights and health laws.'"

"And he already knew about all that?" Connie asked.

"Yeah, he really learned a lot from the rabbi. So then I asked what he knew about the other kind of law. I said that in addition to the civil and ceremonial laws, there was *the law*, also called the Ten Commandments. This was different from the other laws, much like the United States Constitution is different from civil law. Except that the Ten Commandments are even more binding than the Constitution. They're set in stone. Literally."

"So did Alex agree that there's a difference between the ceremonial laws and the law?"

"Well, I think he understood. I tried to explain that the ceremonial laws referred to the system of sacrifices and feasts. God created those laws to portray the plan of salvation. He wanted the people to understand His love and His willingness to die for them."

Clark paused. "You know, Alex was trying really hard to follow everything I said. He told me, 'I'd never thought about that. How about the other laws?'"

"So then we talked about the sabbath laws. I told him that *sabbath* means 'rest.' The ceremonial laws talked about all kinds of sabbaths, in addition to the Sabbath mentioned in the Ten Commandments. Leviticus 23:37, 38 calls them 'sabbaths of the Lord.' Some occurred monthly, others yearly.

"Finally I asked him, 'Which sabbaths do you think Paul was talking about in Colossians and Ephesians? Which ordinances were nailed to the cross—the Ten Commandments, which are God's eternal law, or the ceremonial laws that pointed to Jesus' death on the cross?'"

"And his answer was?" Connie asked.

"Take a guess."

"Humph?" Connie laughed.

"You're right! He started writing furiously on his yellow pad again. I let him finish his notes, then I told him I wanted to mention one more thing. I said, 'In one sense, our relationship to the law *was* changed after the cross.'"

"Didn't that confuse him?" Connie asked.

"Yeah, it did. He said, 'A minute ago you told me the law wasn't done away with at the cross, and now you're changing things? Was it or wasn't it?'

"I explained that it wasn't the *law*, but our *relationship* to it that changed," Clark continued. "We looked up what Paul says about the law in Romans."

Clark flipped over his sheet of notes. "First I showed him where Paul makes it very clear that people are not saved by keeping the law. I read him Galatians 2:16, where it says we're not justified by doing what the law requires. In other words, we can't earn our salvation. Then we read Galatians 3:24, where Paul says we're justified, or saved, only by faith."

Connie interrupted, "I think that's why some people think the law isn't important in a Christian's life."

"You're right," Clark said, "and Paul deals with that very issue in Romans 3:20, where he writes that the law cannot save us, but it points out what sin is. In Romans 4:15 he says that without the law there would be no sin. That's because one of the biblical definitions of sin is breaking the law, like it says in 1 John 3:4. You can't break a law that doesn't exist."

"Just like no one would get speeding tickets if we didn't have speed limits," Connie added.

"Exactly. If sin is breaking God's law, then the law has to be there to break."

"That's a good way to put it," Connie agreed. She set her empty mug on the coffee table and turned to face Clark. "What did Alex think?"

"Well, he cocked his head a little. I told him we need Jesus because we're sinners. We're sinners because we're lawbreakers. If you do away with the law, you no longer need a Saviour. That's exactly what the devil's been trying to tell us for a thousand years."

"Was he still taking notes?" Connie asked.

"He sure was. I tried to pause long enough for him to get everything down. Then I shared Romans 7:12, where Paul says God's law is 'holy, righteous and good' [NIV]. God's law isn't the problem. It's us. We're sinners. Romans 3:23 and 6:23 say that because we violate that law, we stand condemned by it. The law just shows us that we're in rebellion against God."

Connie's eyes twinkled as she listened to her excited husband tell about his conversation with Alex. "So did you ever tell him the good news about the law?" she asked.

Clark grinned. "Hold on, I was just getting to that. I told him that the new covenant talks about God's desire to restore our lives. In Hebrews 8:6, 10, it says that He wants to write His law on our hearts. That's the change that takes place when we're saved. God gives us the desire to obey and then works in our hearts to make it possible. Like Paul says in Romans 6, we're no longer slaves to sin. We don't have to break the law.

"And here's what I really wanted Alex to hear," Clark drummed his fingers on his open Bible as he spoke faster. "When we say it's impossible to keep God's law, we aren't giving Him enough credit. We're basically saying that God isn't powerful enough to live out His will in our lives."

"How did you tie that into the Sabbath?" Connie asked.

"I told him that I don't worship on Sabbath just because it was written on stone at Mount Sinai. Neither do I keep it to be saved. That wouldn't earn me any points with God. I worship on the Sabbath because God has written His law on my heart, and His desires are my desires. I want to please Him, and I want to fellowship with Him on His day."

Connie nodded. "That's what appealed to me when we first learned about the Sabbath," she said. "I don't see it as a rule I have to keep, but as an appointment made at Creation and renewed at Calvary. It's like a date with the God who loved me enough to create me and save me."

"Well, I really believe Alex is trying to understand why this day is so important to us," Clark said.

"Did he say anything else?" Connie asked.

Clark shook his head. "Nothing. But I know he's thinking. And tomorrow I'm having lunch with him again."

CHAPTER 3

Alex lay awake most of that night.

"Well, I hope Clark's happy, because his crazy ideas are sure ruining my sleep," he grumbled to himself.

At 3:00 a.m. he stood up and headed for the kitchen. Deep in thought, he began brewing a pot of water for tea. After rummaging through the pantry, he discovered the biscotti Melanie had hidden from the kids. He poured a cup of hot water, dunked a tea bag, and sat down in the den to think.

On one hand, perhaps he ought to fire Clark immediately. *Then I'd be done hearing about Clark's ideas*, he thought.

Still, he was curious. He'd spent more than an hour after work reading and rereading what Clark had shown him in the Bible. Everything added up. Those texts in Colossians and Ephesians weren't talking about the Ten Commandments—no matter how you tried to turn them.

Years before, Alex had learned in Sunday school that God wants to write His law on the hearts of believers. When it applied to things like stealing or adultery or lying, it made perfect sense. Now he couldn't think of an honest reason that it couldn't also apply to the seventh-day Sabbath.

"I guess I can't walk on both sides of the

fence," he muttered. "Either none of God's law applies to my life, or it all does."

Nobody can be saved by keeping the law, no matter how hard he or she tries. Both Alex and Clark agreed on that. And Alex also knew that Clark was right about obedience. It's the result of letting God live in the heart.

Alex smiled a little as he remembered an illustration he had used in his own Sunday school class. "Obedience to God's commands is the fruit that naturally grows in your life when you have a relationship with Him," he remembered telling his class members. "Apples don't make a tree an apple tree, but an apple tree always produces apples."

A creak in the hall startled Alex. Turning, he saw his wife standing in the dim light. "What in the world are you doing up at this hour drinking tea and eating my biscotti?" she asked, a sleepy grin barely visible on her face.

Tying the belt on her green silk robe, she tiptoed across the room to the couch. "I thought Santa was the only one who ate cookies in the middle of the night."

"Mel, I can't sleep. I didn't tell you about my conversation with Clark Hanson. He told me things I've never heard before."

"Like what, Al?" Melanie brushed back her long red hair and settled onto the couch beside Alex. Snuggling up against him, she asked, "What's going on?"

"I'm still sorting it out myself," Alex sighed.

He tucked his chin into Melanie's soft hair and told her everything he could remember about his Bible study with Clark.

Almost six hours later Alex and Melanie remained curled up on the sofa. Sometime in the night they had drifted to sleep. Snickers from Denae and Little Al awakened them. A few seconds later the bulldog, Toots, landed in their laps.

"Denae, it's 8:40! Why didn't you get us up?" Melanie exclaimed.

"I'm sorry, Mama. I just didn't wake up."

"Nobody did," Melanie laughed and poked Alex in the ribs to get him moving. "C'mon, you guys, time to get going around here. You're late for school, so how about we take a field trip to the zoo? It won't kill you to miss school for a day." She grinned mischievously. "Can you come with us, Alex?"

He shook his head. "I wish I could, but I've got city council today."

After dressing and grabbing a few bagels, Alex paused on his way out the door. "Pray for me, Mel," he said. "I'm confused. Who knows where this could lead?"

She nodded.

❦

Alex wasted no time after lunch that day. "Clark, I've done a lot of thinking about what you said yesterday. It really disturbed me."

The men had finished their sandwiches and were sitting in Alex's office. He continued, "I spent a good share of last night trying to work it all out, and I have some questions."

"OK," Clark answered. "I don't know if I can answer them, but I'll try."

"Doesn't the Bible teach that Jesus changed the day of worship from the seventh-day Sabbath to Sunday in celebration of the Resurrection?" Alex asked. "As you said, He made the Sabbath holy after Creation. But after He rose from the dead, didn't He change it to the first day of the week? That's what I've always been told."

Brushing the last crumbs off his lap, Clark answered, "If it's true that Jesus changed the day, then the religious world is absolutely right in worshiping on the first day of the week, and I've been wrong. Where did you find that it was changed?"

"Well, actually I didn't," Alex admitted. "I looked up all the texts on the first day of the week in the Bible, and only one seems to come close."

"That's the point, Alex. The Gospels contain a tremendous amount of material from Jesus' life. He wasn't the kind of guy to beat around the bush. He wasn't afraid to state His convictions. Yet not one Gospel writer records that He changed His holy Sabbath."

"That's what bothers me," Alex said. "I looked everywhere in the concordance. I tried looking up 'Sunday,' 'first day of the week,' and even 'day after the Sabbath.' It just isn't there."

"Well, as far as I know, the first day of the week is mentioned six times in the Gospels—

in Matthew 28:1; Mark 16:2, 9; Luke 24:1; and John 20:1, 19," Clark commented. "In each case, the verses mention that Jesus was buried on the preparation day, which is now called Friday. Then He rested in the tomb on the Sabbath and rose on the first day of the week. It's sort of like saying that I went to my grandparents' house on Friday, relaxed with them on Saturday, and came home on Sunday. Just the facts are stated. You can't find any hint of change."

Alex leaned forward and asked, "How about after the Resurrection, though? Didn't Jesus always meet with His disciples on Sunday? That was my impression."

Clark scratched his head and spoke slowly, "As I remember, the Bible mentions just a few specific times that Jesus met with His disciples after the Resurrection. First, He met several of them on the day of the Resurrection—to tell them He was alive. That story appears in all four Gospels. John, in his account, adds that they were all shut away in the upper room. Since they were afraid of the Jews, they were hiding when Jesus appeared to them. Nowhere does the text imply that this was a worship service."

"But I bet they were doing a lot of praying," Alex remarked.

Clark smiled. "Yeah, I'm sure you're right," he agreed. "They no doubt were afraid of meeting the same fate He had. He came that day to calm them down, offer them peace, and promise the Holy Spirit. He didn't say anything about changing the day of worship."

Alex nodded. "OK, that's the first time He met with them. What about the other times?"

"The Bible says He appeared to them again eight days later, which would make it a Monday. That story comes toward the end of John 20. And another time was 40 days later." Clark grabbed a pencil and did a rough calculation. "I guess that would make it a Friday."

"What about the time Jesus appeared when the disciples were out fishing?" Alex asked.

"Yes, that story's in John 21," Clark nodded. "But we know that couldn't have been a day of worship, because they were catching fish."

Alex turned to a blank page in his notebook and continued writing. Finally he laid down his pencil and looked up. "You know, I'd almost forgotten a text. What can you possibly do with Revelation 1:10? It clearly states that John was in the spirit on the Lord's day."

"Let's look at it for a minute," Clark answered. "Where does the text define what day of the week is the Lord's day?"

"Well, I don't know." Alex picked up his pencil again and chewed on the end. "I guess it doesn't. I just assumed, I mean, I think everyone assumes it's Sunday. What do you think?"

"Revelation 1:10 doesn't say," Clark said. "But Mark 2:27, 28 gives us a hint." Alex leaned over to watch as Clark turned to the new text.

"Jesus talks to His disciples here," Clark

explained. "Remember, Jesus is the same Lord referred to in Revelation 1:10. He tells them, 'The Sabbath was made for man, not man for the Sabbath' [NIV]. Then He says that the Son of Man, or Jesus, 'is Lord even of the Sabbath' [NIV]. As far as I know, that's the only place where Jesus is called Lord of a certain day, and it's the Sabbath, not the first day of the week."

Alex studied the text and then turned back to Revelation. "So you're saying that this 'day of the Lord' is the seventh day?"

"Well, not everyone agrees about that," Clark answered. "But don't you think it seems possible?"

Alex shrugged. "It works for me," he said. "How about Acts 20:7 and 1 Corinthians 16? That's where the disciples are worshiping on the first day of the week. This was just after Jesus ascended to heaven, so some kind of change must have taken place."

"Let's look at the verses," Clark suggested.

Alex frowned and turned the pages of his Bible so quickly that he almost ripped them out of the book. "OK, we'll look, but you'll have to do some tall convincing. They're obviously worshiping on Sunday here."

Pointing his finger at Acts 20:7, Alex read, "'On the first day of the week, we came together to break bread. Paul spoke to the people and, because he intended to leave the next day, kept on talking until midnight' [NIV]. In this verse, you have Paul preaching and the

Christians taking Communion. What more do you want?"

Looking Alex in the eye, Clark asked, "Where does it say they celebrated Communion?"

"They broke bread," Alex answered. "That's Communion, isn't it?"

"Is it? How about Acts 2:46, 47? What does it say?"

Alex turned to the passage and read, "'Every day they continued to meet together in the temple courts. They broke bread in their homes and ate together with glad and sincere hearts, praising God and enjoying the favor of all the people.'"

"First of all, for discussion's sake, let's assume that breaking bread means they were celebrating Communion," Clark said. "If Communion could occur on any day of the week, it wouldn't make the day sacred. In that case, Tuesday would be just as holy as Saturday or Sunday worship."

Clark continued, "But I don't think that's the point in this text. 'Breaking bread' doesn't seem to refer to Communion in Acts. Probably they were just eating together."

Exasperated, Alex pressed his lips together, wiped his red face, and spoke again. "OK, OK, perhaps 'breaking bread' is eating dinner, not Communion. But Paul was still preaching, and it was the first day of the week. You can't get around that."

Clark gingerly asked, "Alex, do you have your other Bible here? The one with parallel versions?"

"Yeah. Why?"

"Look up this passage in the *New English* or *Living Bible*," Clark urged.

Alex spun around in his chair and snatched his parallel Bible from the credenza. Opening it to Acts 20:7, he read "'On the Saturday night, in our assembly for the breaking of bread, Paul, who was to leave the next day, addressed them, and went on speaking until midnight'" (NEB).

Confused, Alex scowled. "What in the . . . what is this talking about, Clark?"

"Do you remember," Clark answered, "how each day is described in the Creation story in Genesis?"

"Well, it says that evening and morning were the first day, and so on. What's that have to do with anything?"

"When the Bible describes a day, Alex, the evening comes first. In other words, the dark part of a 24-hour period comes before the morning, or light part. If Paul was preaching during the dark portion of the first day of the week, what would we call it today?"

Alex sat for more than a minute, staring at the verse in Acts. "I guess we'd call it Saturday night," he said, "which means that Paul probably started preaching on Sabbath and preached on until midnight because he was leaving the next day and didn't know when he'd see them again."

"You're right. That's exactly what it means."

Alex looked from one Bible version to the other. "I don't know what to make of this. I, uh,

I think I've had about enough Bible study for one day. Would you mind excusing me? I know you've got work to do, and I need some time to think."

"Sure." Clark stood and reached for the door. With his hand on the knob, he turned. "Alex, I know this is tough for you. And confusing. Connie and I did a lot of wondering when we heard about all this a few years ago."

"It's just that, well, this goes against everything I've been taught," Alex replied.

Clark nodded. "I know. I'll be praying for you as you sort it out."

For an hour Alex sat alone in his office, gazing at the open Bibles. At last he pulled on his jacket and headed for home.

CHAPTER 4

"OK, here's my only chance," Alex mumbled. He was down to the final text. Just one. But that was all he needed if it was the right text.

He knew this was his last line of defense, so he wanted to be sure before he showed the verse to Clark. He also wanted time to pray.

When he reached home that afternoon, he changed into blue sweats and a clean white T-shirt. Then he poured himself a cup of coffee and retired to the den with a Bible. Melanie had gone to her aerobics class.

Kneeling beside his chair, he prayed, "Lord, 20 years ago I promised to follow wherever You led. I've done my best to serve You. Your Word is precious to me, and I've tried to obey Your laws. Now I'm having a rough time. Please straighten out this Sabbath business so Melanie and I will have no doubts. I pray this in the name of Jesus. Amen."

Opening his Bible, Alex sat down and read 1 Corinthians 16:1-3. In this passage Paul encouraged the Corinthian believers to give a generous offering when they met for church on the first day of the week. At least that's what he'd always believed. If that was the case, then they were already worshiping on Sunday when Paul was alive.

Paul would have come down hard on the

believers if they were worshiping on the wrong
day. Clearly the day of worship must have
been changed.

Alex sighed. He had to be sure about his facts.
If he was wrong, then he had an empty gun.

"'Now about the collection for God's people,'" he read to himself. "'Do what I told the
Galatian churches to do. On the first day of every
week, each one of you should set aside a sum of
money in keeping with his income, saving it up,
so that when I come no collections will have to
be made. Then, when I arrive, I will give letters
of introduction to the men you approve and send
them with your gift to Jerusalem'" (NIV).

That seemed pretty straightforward. But
what did it mean? The verse didn't really mention a worship service. In fact, Paul seemed to be
talking to individuals rather than a group. He
was telling them to set aside their offering on the
first day of the week.

Alex remembered hearing how the church in
Jerusalem had undergone tremendous persecu-
tion. Paul had encouraged other churches to
send love offerings to help support them. On the
first day of each week, the members were supposed to set aside their gifts individually. But
why on the first day?

Then again, why not? As Alex considered
the problem, he realized it all made sense for
people who worshiped on Sabbath. When
Friday came, they shut down their businesses
and rested. On Sunday morning, when they to-

taled up the previous week's receipts, they set aside the offering.

Alex also recalled reading that the gifts given by the Corinthian believers probably weren't cash. Instead, they gave items used in their own trades. The economy was based on barter because only the wealthy had actual money. Obviously Paul couldn't carry large gifts, so they needed to be converted to hard currency. It was something that needed to be done ahead of time.

"Maybe 1 Corinthians 16 doesn't show early Christians worshiping on Sunday either," Alex concluded. "So when did Paul go to church?"

Reaching for his concordance and the ever-present yellow notebook, Alex padded into the kitchen for more coffee. "I can't believe this," he muttered. A clear pattern emerged as he studied, and the pattern grew clearer every time he opened his Bible.

Slowly he turned from text to text. Acts 13:14. Acts 13:42-44. Acts 16:13. Acts 17:2-4. Acts 18:3, 4. In all cases he found Paul worshiping with both Jewish and Gentile Christians. And in all cases, they met on the seventh-day Sabbath.

A funny feeling settled in Alex's stomach. He feared that something major was about to change in his life. He didn't know where it would lead, but he knew he'd have to come to terms with it.

He pulled on his running shoes, scribbled a note to Melanie, and whistled for Toots. With the bounding dog at his side, he headed toward the park so he could think.

CHAPTER 5

"Mike, I need to talk to you. Could you give me a call?" Alex put down the phone, hoping that Mike would check his answering machine soon.

Mike Silver, the young pastor of a large suburban church, played racquetball with Alex three mornings a week at the YMCA. Intelligent and deeply spiritual, he had become a close friend. Although the Bowens didn't attend his church, Mike and Alex prayed together after their games and often talked about how God was leading in their lives. Alex knew he could talk candidly with Mike.

"Hi, Al, I got your message," Mike said when he called an hour later. "What's up?"

"I need to talk to someone, and I don't want to upset my pastor until I know where I'm headed. I think he may be a little defensive about what I want to discuss. What's the chance of lunch together tomorrow?"

"Sure; where do you want to meet?"

"How about my place? Melanie can make us a pot of soup and some sandwiches, and we can talk privately."

"Great, I've wanted to see where you live anyway. Al, is everything OK? This sounds pretty ominous."

"Yeah, it's fine. I guess. I mean, I'm not leaving my wife, I haven't had an affair, and business is great. It's just that I've been studying some things in the Bible that are new to me."

"And you're sure you don't want to talk to your pastor?"

"I know I need to talk to him. But not yet. I need someone neutral to give me a listening ear without being shocked. When I'm sure what the questions are, then I'll talk to him."

"Hey, buddy, that's fine," Mike responded. "I'll be there at noon tomorrow. Want me to bring my Bible?"

"Yes, please do."

❦

Melanie made the best minestrone soup in the world. Alex was sure of that. He smiled as he watched her cut onions for the broth. Soon the aroma of vegetables, meat, beans, and a secret blend of herbs filled the house. Soup and fresh cornbread—it was so Southern that his accent became three shades heavier just smelling it. Melanie turned to the sink for a minute, and he slipped behind her, picked up the big wooden spoon, and sneaked a quick taste.

The doorbell rang, and Melanie turned to catch him in the act. Chasing him down the hall, she threw a towel after him and shook her finger playfully. Alex scooped up the towel and opened the door to find Mike sniffing appreciatively.

"Is this the way food always smells around here?" he asked. "Man, the whole neighborhood smells great. What's cooking?"

Alex laughed. "When you taste her mine-strone, you'll know why Mel's rated the best cook in this part of town." He moved back so Mike could step through the doorway. "Here, let me take your coat," he added. "If you want to wash up before we eat, it's the first door on the left. Melanie's dishing up the soup."

❀

"Melanie richly deserves her reputation," Mike declared as he finished his second bowl of soup. "Do you share the recipe, or is it a guarded secret?" he asked her.

"We'll see," she answered. "First, how about some chocolate chip cookies?"

"I really shouldn't, but I'll eat one if you're going to twist my arm," Mike laughed. "Charlene keeps me a secret stash in a cookie tin in my study. She says it's supposed to keep my disposition sweet, but I've discovered it just adds to the calories I have to burn off in racquetball."

"Well, you guys get started with your talk, and I'll bring the cookies right out," Melanie said, disappearing into the kitchen.

"Won't you join us?" Mike called. "We can help you clear the table first."

Ten minutes later they all sat down in the living room with their Bibles. "Al, you sounded pretty concerned on the phone," Mike began. "What's up?"

"Well, two weeks ago I hired a new em-ployee," Alex explained. "His name's Clark

Hanson, and he's the best draftsman I've ever had. He's up-to-date, he's quick, he's careful. He's doing the work of the man he replaced, and then some.

"Things were going great until he came to me on Thursday afternoon the first week and told me he needed Saturdays off. Every Saturday. He said he believes God wants him to worship on the seventh day of the week.

"You can imagine my reaction. Saturday's the day we catch up on all the back work. I expect all my employees to be there—it's mandatory. Sometimes we knock off at noon if we get caught up, but not before. So this guy, Clark, said that he'd work extra on other days, but he still couldn't miss his appointment with God each week."

Mike listened quietly as Alex finished the story. "Frankly, he had me over a barrel. I need him, and I know he'd raise the standard of work in the whole drafting department. But I can't let just one person off. Everyone else would give me flak."

"So what did you do?" Mike asked.

"Melanie and I decided that maybe persuasion would work. We spent the weekend studying all the worship texts in the Bible. We even invited Francis Baldwin, my pastor, over for lunch after church. He shared a number of arguments against worship on the seventh-day Sabbath, but he didn't seem too enthusiastic about it."

"And he said he'd pray for us," Melanie added.

Alex nodded. "That night we listed what we thought were 10 irrefutable statements about worship, and I met with Clark for lunch the next day."

"Did you convince him?" Mike asked.

"Hardly!" Alex frowned. "That's the problem! It's been the other way around. He shares ideas with me I've never heard before. Then I come home and show Mel, and we can't find any flaws in them."

"What has he told you?" Mike asked.

Alex pulled his notebook from his briefcase and spent the next hour going over what he and Clark had studied. At last he looked at Mike and asked, "Well, what do you make of it? If Clark Hanson is right, then most of the Christian church is dead wrong."

Mike tipped back in his chair and closed his eyes thoughtfully. "Alex, you've been honest with me," he said, "so now I'm going to do the same with you." He opened his eyes and leaned forward. "If you're looking for someone to disagree with Clark Hanson, then I think you've chosen the wrong man."

"What?" Alex and Melanie looked at each other in surprise.

"Three of us pastors here in town have been getting together regularly to pray and study," Mike explained. The Holy Spirit has worked powerfully in our lives. One area we've been studying is the Sabbath. I can't tell you who the other guys are, but I can tell you how I feel."

Mike hesitated, struggling to choose his words carefully. "I'm convinced," he said, "that the Christian world has forgotten something incredibly important when it comes to the Sabbath."

Again Alex and Melanie exchanged glances. Mike held up his hands. "Now wait," he added. "I'm still studying it myself. I'm just in transition, but our family has made some big changes in the past few months. Accepting the idea of the seventh-day Sabbath would have serious implications for us, so we're moving slowly."

"But what about your church?" Melanie asked. "You're a pastor!"

"I don't know about the future," Mike admitted. "But what I've discovered is the most exciting concept since I first accepted Jesus in my life."

"What about us?" Melanie asked. "Can you help us with our study?" She reached for the cookie plate and offered it to both men again. Mike shook his head, then grinned and took one more.

"First," he said, "let me give you a little background. I think it'll help you understand." He reached for his wallet and pulled out a worn photograph. Melanie and Alex leaned over to see the family snapshot.

"That's me, my parents, and the rest of our family," Mike explained. "I come from generations of compulsive workers. That's how my mom and dad lived, and that's how they trained us. So I'm a natural workaholic."

He replaced the photo and continued. "I

hated the treadmill that my folks lived on. Never saw them. Didn't even know them. We belonged to a church, but we never went to a service unless it was Easter. I promised myself that when I grew up, my family would be different."

He grinned wryly. "And now I'm a pastor. I don't know how many pastors you know, but let me tell you, it's intense. It's probably one of the most time-consuming professions in the world. One of my friends tried to warn me when I went into the ministry. He said, 'Mike, you'll love the ministry, but there's one thing you'll have to come to terms with. You'll never be able to go to bed knowing that the work is done. You'll always have more to do. Pace yourself. Set limits, or your ministry will eat you alive.'"

"Good advice for all of us," Alex commented.

"Sure is, and I wish I'd listened to him!" Mike said. "Charlene and I started the Alder Valley church right after we got married. It was exhilarating to see our efforts rewarded. The church loved us. We were needed in the community. But the church grew, I started working 16 or 18 hours a day, and things changed.

"Our day of reckoning finally came on a family vacation in Minnesota. It was the first time we'd all been alone in more than five years. I watched my kids playing and realized I hardly knew them. I'd been spending very little time with my family. My wife and I were becoming strangers."

Mike took off his glasses and looked at them

for a while. "You know," he continued, "it hurt to admit this, but we even wondered whether we still loved each other. Our relationship was just motions. Nothing but 'Good morning,' 'Goodbye,' or 'Can you take Evan to his basketball game?'"

"But you've always had such a good relationship with your church members," Alex commented.

"Yeah, but even my friendship with God was in trouble. Oh, I was preaching sermons that people drove across town to hear. The church membership was exploding. But deep inside I was an empty shell. I wanted to be a man of God, but the business of my ministry shoved Him out of my life.

"We finally woke up on that vacation and decided we had to do something. But where to start? We were wrestling with an octopus, and there was no way to let loose."

"So what happened?" Alex asked.

"Well, one day my assistant pastor stuck his head in my office door and showed me a book called *A Pause for Peace*. It was written by a Jew who had converted to Christianity. Clifford Goldstein, his name was. I'd never heard of the book, but my assistant said he was curious and wanted to ask me some questions about it. I took it home, threw it on the stack by my bed, and forgot about it.

"The title of that book reached out to me every time I went in the bedroom," Mike continued. "*A Pause for Peace*. Just what I needed. But I didn't have time for it, so I put another book on top of it so I wouldn't see it. Finally I took an afternoon off and read it."

"Was it any good?" Alex asked, reaching for his pen to write down the title.

"Good? It changed my life. The author starts out by describing me exactly. He details this rat race that most American Christians find themselves in. He talks about how we become so involved that soon no time remains for what really matters, like family and God. Then he describes the solution."

"Moving to a cabin in the wilderness?" Melanie suggested. Both she and Alex sat on the edge of their chairs, fascinated.

"Not quite," Mike answered. "See, God knew our needs when He designed us. He issued a divine edict, as king of the universe, guaranteeing that we would have quality time with Him and each other. Genesis says that God spent six days creating the physical part of our world. On the seventh day He created a memorial in time. He set aside 24 hours every week for holy use."

"The theory sounds a lot like what Clark said," Alex nodded. "So, Mike, how does this work in the real world?"

"Beautifully. Even though Charlene and I had been involved with good things, we found ourselves overworked and exhausted. But God invited us to come to Him and rest on His special day. In reality, it's like a bridge that reaches across time and lets us share a little taste of Eden. He washes away the stress and rejuvenates us for the new week. We celebrate our love together. We worship, relax, walk outdoors, laugh, and play."

Melanie looked wistful. "It sounds as if God loves us so much that He really wants to spend uninterrupted time with us every week," she said.

"Yes, that's exactly right," Mike said. "As I read that book, I realized why the devil has done so much to hide the seventh-day Sabbath from people. The Sabbath allows our love affair with God to blossom, and Satan hates it!"

"But don't you still preach on Sunday?" Alex asked.

"Yes, but our family has also started keeping the Sabbath at home. I've fallen in love with my wife again. And I've gotten to know my kids." Mike proudly pulled another photo out of his wallet and passed it to Melanie. "You know," he said, "I found out that I have some really great children. Most of all, I'm discovering a sweeter relationship with God than I ever dreamed possible."

"But what do you actually *do* on the Sabbath?" Alex asked.

"The Bible says Sabbath is a 24-hour period stretching from sunset to sunset," Mike answered, "so we set that time aside. We've developed some special Silver family traditions."

"Like Christmas traditions?" Melanie asked.

"That's the idea, but we get to enjoy them every week. First, we make Friday a day of preparation. Charlene does her Sabbath cooking beforehand so she doesn't have to spend the day in the kitchen. It's like when you have guests, and you try to get things ready ahead of time so you can be with them."

Melanie smiled as Mike continued. "We also try to have the house clean before sundown on Friday night," he said. "We learned some good ideas about that from a book by Abraham Heschel, a Jewish rabbi. The Jews have been celebrating Sabbath for thousands of years, and they have some fantastic ideas for making it special. Heschel describes the Sabbath as a queen who comes every week to visit. We mentioned that idea to the kids and asked them how they would want the house to look for the queen of England. They caught on fast. Now they really enjoy getting the house ready for our Sabbath queen."

"And I'm sure Charlene feels better just having a clean house once a week," Melanie commented.

"You can say that again," Mike agreed. "A little before sundown on Friday, we prepare for our welcoming celebration. The TV goes off, we play our favorite Christian music on the stereo, and we light candles all over the house. As the sun sets, our home fills with the heavenly aroma of Charlene's cooking. She always makes a special meal to welcome God to our house on the Sabbath. Sometimes it's potato soup and scones, some times cornbread and strawberries, other times hot fruit soup and toast."

"You're making me hungry again," Alex laughed.

Mike grinned. "I think some of Melanie's minestrone would work just as well," he said. "As the sun sets, we gather in the living room and welcome God and His Sabbath queen into our home. We pray, sing, and thank Him for who He is and all that He's done. After our candlelight dinner, we share stories or read to the kids. We laugh and cry and take time to know each other. No rush, no deadlines."

"I bet the kids love all the attention," Alex remarked.

"Sure they do," Mike said. "But on Friday nights the kids go to bed early. So do Charlene and I. Sometimes we're so tired that we go right to sleep. You'd never believe how great it feels to get nine or ten hours of sleep after a long week."

"Oh, I believe it," Alex said. Melanie nodded in agreement.

"And other times we take the time to enjoy each other."

"Well, that's Friday night," Melanie said. "What do you do on Saturday?"

"Every week it's different," Mike said. "After all, we're just getting started with these Sabbath traditions. Sometimes we visit friends. Or we get outside and hike or ride bikes. Anything that doesn't detract from our sense of God's presence and our focus on each other is fair game. At least two Sabbaths a month we invite another family or two to join us for the day. That gives them the opportunity to discover what it means to celebrate a Sabbath."

"Finally, we close our Sabbath celebration the same way it began," he finished. "We gather at sunset and pray together."

Alex and Melanie sat silently.

Mike sighed. "I love the Sabbath, and I really look forward to the day when we can celebrate the day with other Christians. I don't know when that will be, but I'm praying that it'll happen someday with our church family."

Looking eagerly at Alex and Melanie, he asked, "Can you imagine what it'll be like to worship in heaven? Imagine being in God's presence. Picture the joy, the freedom, the excitement, the music! If Sabbath is a foretaste of heaven, then I think our Sabbath worship should reflect heaven. That's why we should make the Sabbath very special."

"Why don't Christians keep the Sabbath anymore?" Alex asked.

"I'm not sure, but I know one thing. Any church that could catch this vision would be truly irresistible. If my members are open to it, Alder Valley will become that kind of church."

"Mike, that's beautiful," Melanie said softly, wiping her eyes and glancing at Alex. "I want so much to experience what you've just described."

"You can, Melanie," Mike assured her. "God's Sabbath blessings are available to anyone who gives Him the time."

"Some people in your church aren't going to understand this," Alex pointed out.

"True," Mike answered. "I honestly can't tell you how this will all shake out in our lives. But I do know that God is leading us, and He wants us to tell others. If my church can accept it, praise the Lord."

"And if they can't?" Alex asked.

"Then God must have another ministry planned for me. My Bible study on this has led me to a deeper understanding of God's will. As the spiritual leader of my church, I have to share what I've learned. Of course I'm scared sometimes, but I pray that God will help me make these ideas attractive to my members."

He glanced at his watch and stood to go. "I didn't realize that we'd been talking so long. Melanie, I'd really love a copy of that soup recipe, if you're willing to share."

"I'd be honored," Melanie said as they walked him to the door. "I'll send it with Alex the next time you guys play racquetball. And please tell Charlene that I'd like to meet her."

"All right," Mike agreed as he stepped out the door. "Maybe you ladies can teach us a few things about racquetball."

CHAPTER 6

So, what have you and Alex been talkin' about over lunch lately?" Scorp asked, tossing a new blueprint onto Clark's drafting table and leaning forward, both hands on the desk. "You still trying to convince him to worship on Saturday?"

"What do you mean, Scorp?" Clark asked carefully.

"You know what I mean. The first week you were here, Alex talked to me about your wanting Saturdays off. So I lent him some books I had on the subject. It doesn't take a whole lot of intelligence to know what you guys have been discussing. Anyway, I'd like to have my chance now. Let's do lunch today. It's on me."

"Sure, I'd like that," Clark answered. "Give me about an hour, and I'll be able to break loose."

After finding a corner table at Antonelli's Pizza and ordering their lunch, Scorp got right to the point. "Clark, I've been watching you, and you're a nice guy, but you've got some things to learn about religion and the Bible."

"Oh?" Clark looked up. "That's probably true."

"You're dead wrong about the Sabbath! The fourth commandment is part of the law, but we're under grace. Therefore, we're not required to keep it. People like you confuse folks with talk about the Sabbath. You're putting them under bondage, just like the Pharisees did in Jesus' day."

Clark started to speak, but Scorp continued. "I don't know what you've been telling Alex, but you better not be filling his mind with nonsense. He's a tremendous Christian, but he's no theologian. If I have to, I'll nail your hide to the wall to stop you from spreading your ideas. Do we understand each other?"

Clark prayed silently as Scorp ranted. When an opening came, he said, "Scorp, I agree with you that Christians are under grace, not the law. But that doesn't release us from keeping that law."

Clark paused while the waiter set their pizza and soft drinks on the table. "My understanding," he said, "is that to be under the law means to be under its condemnation. It means to be under a sentence of death because we've broken it. To be under grace, on the other hand, is to experience God's forgiveness through Jesus."

Lifting several pieces of steaming pizza to his plate, Scorp asked sarcastically, "So?"

"Forgiveness doesn't mean that we're free to break the law again. If I break a law and get caught, I still have to go to court, right? I stand under the condemnation of the law. Now, say the judge takes mercy on me and pardons me. Does that give me the right to go out and break the law again? If the governor pardons me for murder, can I kill someone else?"

"No," Scorp answered warily.

"It seems to me that those who are forgiven, if they have any gratitude at all, will want to keep the law *because* they're forgiven," Clark finished.

"But Paul says no one can be saved by keeping the law," Scorp countered. "No matter how hard you try, you'll never be good enough to be saved."

"You're absolutely right!" Clark nodded as he reached for his second slice of pizza. "But Paul also says, in Romans 3:31, that we uphold the law by faith. The law isn't canceled by faith. He also says, in 1 Corinthians 7:19, that keeping God's commands is what counts."

Scorp stopped in the middle of his mouthful. Choking it down, half chewed, he retorted, "You're not a Christian if you think you're saved by keeping the law. That's Jewish legalism through and through."

"Scorp, let's settle one thing right now. No human has ever kept the law well enough to be saved. But you're missing the point. For example, when you're out surveying, do you ever use your transit for a shovel?"

"Don't be stupid! What're you driving at?"

"A transit wasn't designed to shovel dirt, and using it that way would destroy it, right? But just because you don't use a transit as a shovel doesn't mean that a transit doesn't have a purpose. The same is true for God's law. We both agree that we're not saved by keeping the law. That's not what it was designed for."

"Agreed. So exactly what is the purpose of the law?" Scorp muttered.

"In Romans 3:20 and 7:7 Paul says that the purpose of the law is to show us when we sin. And Romans 5:13 says that God couldn't legitimately charge us as sinners if there wasn't a law for us to break. The Sabbath is part of that law. In fact, it's the only part that most Christians disagree with."

"Listen," Scorp interrupted, "this Sabbath is part of the Old Testament law. We're not bound by that."

"OK, just for example, let's say someone asked if he could sleep with your wife," Clark said. "I know you'd refuse. And then he'd ask, 'Why not?' You'd open the Bible and point to the Ten Commandments. In the Old Testament. The same would be true for lying, stealing, and swearing.

"But," Clark continued, "if someone mentions the seventh-day Sabbath, suddenly you say the law has been done away with. You can't have both sides of the argument, Scorp. If all 10 are done away with, then we can lie, cheat, steal, and sleep with other men's wives. If the law is still in effect, we should live by all of it."

Scorp wasn't about to be bested by a draftsman 20 years his junior. Wiping his mouth with a napkin, he said, "OK, I'll buy your argument that obedience is important. But it doesn't involve the old law. The Ten Commandments were part of the old covenant. Paul says we're now under a new covenant, which frees us from obeying the old law." With that, he grabbed another slice of pizza.

"But covenants in the Bible are agreements concerning the law, not the law itself," Clark responded. "In fact, the word *covenant* means 'agreement,' not 'law.' The old covenant, if I understand it correctly, was Israel's agreement to keep the law in their own strength, by works. They failed, as will anyone who tries it. We both know that. The new covenant is altogether different."

"And how might that be?" Scorp challenged.

"First of all, it's based on better promises. Hebrews 8 tells us that the old covenant was based on faulty promises—Israel's and ours. Our own promises may sound good, but they aren't worth much. In the new covenant, Jesus Himself promises to live in us. The law is written on our hearts. As David says in Psalm 119:174, the law becomes a delight."

Hoping to lighten the conversation, Clark added, "Hey, aren't you glad I delight in the law that prohibits me from murdering you? Otherwise I could get upset and do away with you when you give me a really tough drawing to do at work."

Scorp grinned in spite of himself. "About this Sabbath business," he said. "Don't you realize that it really doesn't make any difference which day of the week you keep, just as long as you observe one day in seven?"

"Really?" Clark answered. "Then why do you insist that we should worship on Sunday?"

"Because everyone else does."

"Not everyone. Less than 50 percent of the people in the United States claim to be active Christians who worship at all. And some of those do worship on Saturday. Many Jews also worship on Saturday, and Muslims keep Friday. Pagans keep all sorts of days. If you were in a Muslim country, would you keep Friday to fit in?"

"Probably not."

"And if you lived in Israel, would you keep Saturday so that you didn't stand out from the rest of the population?"

"No."

"So the issue isn't about fitting in, but about which day is right."

"Clark, the issue isn't the day," Scorp insisted. "Why do you have to make such a big deal over it?" The table shook under his fists, and soda sloshed from their glasses.

"I believe the Sabbath is important because it's important to God," Clark answered. "Do you tell Millie, 'Look, who cares when we celebrate our anniversary? One day's the same as the next'?"

"No, she wouldn't go for that," Scorp said.

"That's right. You celebrate on a particular day because it's important to someone you love. When God repeated His law at Mount Sinai, He told the people to remember the *seventh* day. It's the celebration of our creation. Deuteronomy 5 says that it's also a celebration of our redemption. God never said that just any day would do."

"What counts," Scorp declared, "is the spirit, not the letter, of the law."

"To me, keeping the spirit of the law means that my heart is in it and that I go all out," Clark replied.

Scorp's anger increased. "Listen here, we can't keep the Sabbath that God instituted at Creation anyway," he sputtered. "It's been at least 6,000 years since God made the world. How could we possibly know that we're worshiping on the right day?"

"That's easy," Clark answered. "The same God who created the world reminded His people of the Sabbath when He gave the law to Israel at Mount Sinai. If they'd been off in counting their days, He would have straightened them out. And ever since then, at least some Jews have been keeping the Sabbath. In addition, Jesus could have corrected any errors in the day when He was here on this earth. We have calendars from the time of Jesus, so we know that the weekly cycle is still the same."

"But what about when they changed the calendars a few hundred years ago?" Scorp asked.

"Yeah, I think it was around 1582," Clark went on, "but the days of the week didn't change. The date went from Thursday, October 4, to Friday, October 15, to make up for a whole pile of leap years they'd missed over the centuries. The week was still on schedule. You can find that in any good encyclopedia."

The veins on Scorp's neck stood out as he chewed his last hunk of pizza as if it were bubble gum. Abruptly he changed the subject.

"You know what really gripes me about people like you?" he asked. "You think that you're better than the rest of us. You believe, don't you, that everyone who worships on Sunday has the mark of the beast. Be honest now. You think I'm going to hell because I worship on Sunday."

Scorp spoke faster and faster. "Well, I'm here to tell you, mister, that you're going to be mighty surprised who's in hell one of these days. You're pretty arrogant, you know that, Hanson? You may think that you're the only Christian in the world, but I'm telling you that you're not."

Startled diners looked up from their food as Scorp yelled. "A whole lot of people who worship on Sunday are a lot closer to God than you are. Do you really think that God's going to keep someone out of heaven over a day? Give me a break."

"Scorp," Clark said quietly, "I don't believe you have the mark of the beast because you worship on Sunday. I don't think anybody has the mark right now. But I do think that even small matters can have tremendous significance in God's eyes."

"Give me an example," Scorp demanded.

"Do you think that eating some fruit was important enough to get Adam and Eve kicked out of the Garden of Eden? Yet that's exactly what happened. An apple or apricot, or whatever, may not seem like much. But to God, it symbolized something much greater—their loyalty to Him."

"You're changing the subject," Scorp said.

"Wait," Clark motioned with his hand. "I believe the same kind of dynamics will operate at the end of the world. You're right, a day is a pretty insignificant thing, unless God has given it significance. And He has. The loyalty of people living at the end of the world will be tested by their obedience in honoring a day He's made holy.

"I'm not criticizing those who choose to worship on another day," Clark added. "I'm not the judge. However, I do feel responsible to make people aware of the issue. And I also feel that anyone who hasn't experienced the Sabbath day is missing out on a tremendous blessing."

Scorp rose and stalked from the restaurant. Clark paid the bill and walked back to the office alone.

❧

Alex stopped by Clark's desk that afternoon to ask him to draw a plat for a new project. "Hey," he said, "I missed talking to you at lunch today. I'd like to ask some more questions."

"I ate with Scorp today," Clark answered.

"Oh?"

"I wasn't sure if you wanted to talk, and he offered to buy my meal."

"Did he take you to Antonelli's? Ray Antonelli makes the best pizza in town, but you're guaranteed to need a gallon of Alka-Seltzer by the time supper rolls around. Pretty powerful stuff he puts in those things."

"That's where we ate," Clark nodded. "I haven't suffered too many ill effects so far. Look, if you'd like to meet tomorrow, I'll be glad to brown-bag it with you. I'd be interested to hear what you've been thinking about."

Scorp listened quietly without looking up from his drafting board. He determined to do something about Clark Hanson before Alex was completely messed up.

CHAPTER 7

Y ou're gonna have to do better than that, Skeeterbug!"

Mike remembered the first time he'd heard that phrase. It had been his first varsity game, and Georgia was playing Georgia Tech. When those teams met, it was for blood. He'd been surprised when the huge defensive back extended a hand to help him up. That's how he'd met Deion Maxwell.

Mike was thin and fast in those days. So fast his dad said he was like a mosquito—you kept slapping at him but never caught him. Skeeterbug, that's what they called him.

Deion Maxwell, on the other hand, was big. Big, but so light on his feet that everyone called him Dragonfly. For weeks the papers talked about the matchup between the two players. Every year after that they met on the field when Georgia played Georgia Tech.

That was years ago. Now, as Mike stood on the racquetball court and waited for the next serve from Deion, he remembered staring across the scrimmage line at the same huge guy. He remembered someone as big as a moving van and as fast as an Indy car chasing him down the field.

What had amazed him, though, was how gentle the big giant was. Yeah, he tackled hard enough to leave bruises that lasted for a week, but Deion wasn't ruthless. When the play was over, the big back was always there, grinning, extending a hand to help him up.

Now Deion aced a low shot into the angle between the right wall and the floor. "Get a move on, Skeeterbug," he teased.

Mike remembered what he'd felt like leading Deion to a relationship with Jesus. After graduation, Mike had entered the seminary after turning down a contract with a West Coast team. Deion was drafted by Dallas. In his first professional game, playing first string as a rookie, he'd been hit from his blind side as he set to block a pass. His knee would never be the same, the doctor said. Placed on waivers, he limped home to piece together his life.

And there Mike found him. Sitting in the front room of his mother's house in Macon, they talked and cried and just sat together for a week.

Football, in those days, was more than a game for Deion. It was his future. It was the ticket out of a little white house on the wrong side of the tracks. It was his opportunity to provide education for his brothers and sisters and comfort for his tired mother. Suddenly the future had disappeared. He was doomed to a lifetime in the local furniture factory.

But when Deion accepted Jesus as Saviour and Lord, God led him into a life far beyond anything he'd imagined in the NFL. A year later he met Rio, and they eventually married and had three wonderful children. A surgeon at Emory discovered a way to rebuild his knee. Deion started a company and sold Bibb County furniture all over the South. His mom got a new house, and his brothers and sisters went to college.

And he'd become an excellent racquetball player. *Too good!* Mike thought as Deion drilled another low shot into the corner.

Later, as they dressed after a shower, Deion turned to him. "So, Mike, your car or mine this year?"

Every year the Silver and Maxwell families attended the Georgia/Georgia Tech game together. Every year they ate lunch in the parking lot together. And every year, when lunch was over, they headed toward seats exactly opposite each other. From different sides of the stadium they screamed and hollered for their alma maters.

The press loved the old rivalry. After the game the winner always took the loser's family to the Varsity Café for hamburgers and onion rings.

Reaching for his sweatshirt, Mike replied quietly, "We're not going this year, Deion."

"What?" Deion was stunned. "What do you mean, you're not going? I know ticket prices are up, but I'll help you." He turned and whipped his wet towel into the laundry bin. "Did Georgia sell your seats out from under you? Man, I'll go to the press with this if I have to. This is tradition! Fifteen years of hollering back and forth at each other. You can't be serious!"

"I am. I know it's hard to understand, Deion, but I just can't go."

"Is it me, Mike? I mean, we're still friends, right? Man, if I've done anything to offend you, I'm sorry."

"It's not that. It's something a whole lot bigger and harder to explain."

"You and Charlene aren't having—"

"No, no, Deion, we're great. In fact, that's part of what I want to share with you. Listen, can I buy you lunch? We've gotta talk."

"Sure," Deion answered, pulling out his cellular phone. "Let me call my secretary to cancel a few appointments."

A half hour later they met at an Italian restaurant. "So what is it, man?" Deion asked.

Looking up from a plate of linguine primavera, Mike smiled. "Remember the changes we both went through after college? How playing football became a lot less important?"

"Yeah."

"And remember how God led us both into something a whole lot better than the NFL?"

Deion nodded.

"Well, now God's teaching me something else, Deion. It's another step in what He's doing in my life. I wanted to share it with you before, but first I had to figure it out myself. Anyway, now there's something really important in my life. Even more important than the Georgia game."

"What?"

"You're not going to believe this."

"Try me."

"I'm in love!"

"What?" Deion sputtered. "I thought you told me—"

"Just kidding," Mike laughed. "Well, not really. I've discovered something that's enriching my relationship with God so much, it's like I'm falling in love with Him all over again."

"What is it?"

"It's called the Sabbath."

"The Sabbath? As in rabbis and yarmulkes and candles and the Torah? Are you converting to Judaism?"

"No. I've discovered that God set aside 24 hours every week for me, as a Christian. It's a gift He gave us at Creation, long before Jews existed. Jesus celebrated it. All the apostles celebrated it. It's like He gave us a hidden treasure that we've had in our pockets forever, but we forgot about it. Now I've just discovered it."

"Look, man, have you gotten involved in some cult or something?" Deion asked.

"No, just let me show you something. At Creation God gave us this day of quality time with Him and each other." Pulling a little Bible from the breast pocket of his sport coat, Clark went on. "Mark 2:27, 28 says God gave us the Sabbath as a gift. Every seventh day is special to Him. That's why I can't go to the game with you."

"God doesn't like football?"

"I don't know," Mike laughed. "Maybe He does. But that's not the point. The Sabbath was given to us for a purpose, and I don't feel that football is part of it."

"So what do you do on Saturday?"

"Well, God gave it to us for at least three reasons. The first is for worship."

"As in going to church?"

"Yeah, I suppose so. I'm still trying to figure out how to break this to my congregation, but eventually I hope I can celebrate with them. Next, it's for quality time with my family and friends."

"So, are we not friends?" Deion asked.

"I'm not done, big guy. Let me finish. The time with friends can't detract from the time with God. In other words, I don't go to car races on Sabbath, because the atmosphere doesn't give me a sense of His presence. Same with downhill skiing and even college football.

"And I found out something else as I studied," Mike continued. "Jesus did almost all of His healing miracles on the Sabbath. So the Sabbath is a day for helping others. We're going to start spending a lot of our Sabbath afternoons helping people."

"Like the homeless and that kind of thing?"

"Maybe. All kinds of hurting people. Isaiah 58 gives us a whole list of them. You know, I've always believed that we Christians should be doing more for others, but I've never been able to squeeze out the time. Now I've discovered that God gave us six days for our work, but He reserved the seventh especially for serving Him. Anyway, I'm getting excited about this, and I hope you can join us sometime."

"I don't know, man. You say you got this out of the Bible?"

"Yes, the Bible! Here, let me pick up the check," Mike said as he took the bill. "Why don't you think about it?" he added. "Tech's going to lose anyway, so you might as well come and do something useful. Maybe you won't get depressed for a month like last year."

"You know how to hurt a guy, Skeeterbug," Deion grinned, shaking his head. "I'll think about it, but don't count on anything."

CHAPTER 8

"So I get to meet the young man who's been giving one of my church members so many sleepless nights."

Clark looked up from his computer into the kind eyes of Francis Baldwin, Alex and Melanie's pastor. "They tell me you're quite the Bible student," he added.

With a twinkle in his eyes, he extended his hand. "Don't get up. I was just on my way to see Alex and wanted to introduce myself. I understand we're eating lunch together today." Francis held up a sack lunch in his other hand.

That was the first Clark had heard about the lunch appointment. Surprised, he glanced at the other employees, all staring curiously. "I, uh, I'm looking forward to it," he stammered. Francis smiled and headed for Alex's office.

※

"I really appreciate your visit, Francis." Alex motioned his pastor to a chair and closed the door. "The past couple weeks have been like a roller coaster. I've wanted to discuss something with you, but I needed to sort myself out first. Now I need your help."

"You told me it has to do with your draftsman, Clark Hanson."

"Right. See, his ideas aren't exactly mainstream."

"Something about the day of worship?" Francis asked.

"Yeah. Honestly, I've been impressed that we've been missing something when it comes to the Sabbath. Before Clark comes in, let me ask you a question. Apparently God originally planned for His people to worship with Him on the seventh day of the week. But now practically the whole Christian world worships on Sunday. How did it change?"

"Alex, I wish I could give you a good answer on that. I've been wondering about it myself. I have a friend who's a church historian, so maybe I could talk to him and get our questions answered."

A knock sounded at the door. "Come in," Alex called.

"Am I disturbing a private conversation?" Clark stood in the doorway holding a fast food bag. "I didn't bring a lunch today, so I ran out and grabbed something quick. Hope the smell of these fries doesn't make you guys jealous."

"You're rotten," Alex laughed. "Why don't we eat at the conference table? You can sit at the far end so the aroma will waft the other way."

"Clark," Alex said when they were settled, "I've been telling Francis about what you've told me. I respect his opinion and wanted to get his reaction. You don't mind, do you?"

"No, not at all," Clark answered.

After asking God's blessing on their food, Francis turned to Clark. "I understand you worship on the Sabbath. I'm interested to know why."

"In a nutshell, it's a matter of love and loyalty. Love, because I believe God sets aside a special time for me every week. And loyalty because I chose to make Him Lord of my life when I became a Christian."

"OK, keep going," Francis encouraged.

Clark paused to take a bite. Then he gazed into space, thinking hard.

"You know, I hate taking out the garbage," he began.

Alex and Francis started laughing.

"In fact, I'll do just about anything to avoid it!" Clark said. "But you know, when my wife asks me to take out the trash, I almost enjoy it— because I love her."

Grabbing some more fries, he continued, "When I found out that God set aside 24 hours every week just to spend with me, I had a hard time believing it. But once I was convinced, it became a pleasure to keep that weekly appointment, even when it involved inconvenience at times. The Sabbath has enriched my love affair with God so much that I wouldn't give it up for anything. I guess I shouldn't even compare it to taking out the trash. It's the highlight of my week."

Clark glanced at the pastor and then at his boss. "The other day I read in John 14:15 that if we love God, we'll keep His commandments," he said. "I love Him so much that I want to spend time with Him."

Alex was surprised to see the intensity on Francis' face as he listened.

"Then there's loyalty," Clark said. "Look how Satan has destroyed the gifts God gave us at Creation. He gave us life, the family, and Sabbath. But life is cheap these days. Families are destroyed by divorce, adultery, incest, and pornography. Satan has also gone after God's Sabbath."

"But how do you see this as an issue of loyalty?" Francis asked.

"I guess keeping the Sabbath is a tangible way of showing our loyalty to God," Clark answered. "Just as Satan tried to destroy life and family, he's also attempted to hide the meaning of the Sabbath. In his desire to replace God in our lives, the devil has substituted another day of worship for the one God gave us."

Clark hesitated. "Please don't be offended by this," he added, "but Sunday was the day pagans worshiped the sun. That's why it's called Sunday. I keep the Sabbath because I want to be loyal to my Saviour, not to human beings or traditions."

Alex watched Francis, but couldn't read what the pastor was thinking.

"Go on," Francis said.

"You discover two camps when you come to the book of Revelation," Clark said. "You have those who follow God and those who are loyal to His archenemy. One group receives the seal of God. The other receives the mark of the beast, which is the symbol of Satan's followers in Revelation 12 and 13. Each of the two sides is symbolized by a day. That's where the Sabbath comes in."

Clark held his sandwich with one hand and carefully opened his Bible with the other. "Revelation 14:12 tells us that God's followers are those who have two identifying marks," he went on. "Those marks are faith in Jesus and His sacrifice at Calvary and a commitment to keeping His commandments."

"I'm still not sure why you think this one commandment is more important than the others," Alex interrupted.

"It's not, but it's one that Satan has tried especially hard to destroy. Because of my faith in Jesus and my loyalty to Him, I want to honor all His commandments, including the Sabbath."

"And that's why he won't work on Saturday," Alex said, looking at Francis.

Clark nodded. "That's right. I can't work on that day even if it costs me my job." He glanced at the clock and stood.

"You know, guys, I'd love to talk longer," he said, "but Scorp needs me to finish a drawing for the planning commission meeting. Pastor Baldwin, I hope my honesty hasn't offended you."

Francis shook his head and grasped Clark's extended hand. Clark started to turn, and then spoke again. "I have a lot of Christian friends who worship God on Sunday," he said. "They're sincere followers of Jesus. We enjoy sweet spiritual fellowship together, and some of them are my prayer partners. I know God honors their love and loyalty. But when a person discovers truth from God's Word, even when it goes against ancient traditions, then that person is accountable to God. I hope you understand."

"Oh, I do, Clark, I do. Thank you for your candor. I hope we'll meet again soon."

Long silence followed after Clark closed the door behind him.

"Well?" Alex asked.

"Alex, we've been friends for 25 years," Francis began. "I've buried both of your parents, I've baptized your children, we've vacationed together. So I guess I can be honest with you."

Clearing his throat and staring out the window, he went on. "I don't know where to begin. I'm part of a little group, three pastors. We meet weekly to pray and support each other."

Startled, Alex searched his pastor's face.

Francis explained, "Several months ago we came across this little book on the Sabbath. Now, I'd studied this in seminary, and I knew all the arguments condemning Sabbathkeepers. But I'd honestly never studied with an open mind. I was content to rest on our church traditions."

"And now?" Alex asked slowly.

"I've read all the Bible has to say on the Sabbath. I was stunned and amazed by what I read. It's everything Clark mentioned and a whole lot more."

"You're saying he's right?"

"I wish I could tell you otherwise, but, yes, he's right."

"Then why did you help me make that list of arguments to use against him?" Alex asked.

Tears welled up in Francis's eyes, and he looked away for a long minute. "Alex, this isn't easy. When I shared what I was learning with my wife, she came unglued. She said I was a fanatic, questioned my sanity, and threatened to leave if I ever brought it up again. Then there's my ministry. I'd lose it all if I made my views public. It's the only profession I have."

"What will you do, Francis?" Alex asked.

"I don't know. I'm caught between what I believe is God's will and all that I hold dear. I really don't know."

Wiping his eyes with a napkin, Francis looked up. "Alex, you and Melanie need to follow your conscience on this. It would be a terrible loss if you ever left our church, but you've got to go where God leads you. Promise me you will! And pray I'll have the courage to do what's right."

Sliding his uneaten sandwich back into the brown bag, Francis smiled sadly. "I envy you, Alex, I really do. Maybe someday I'll join you."

CHAPTER 9

Joe Maniscalco patted his broad face with a napkin, burped discreetly, and peered across the table.

"So, Scorp, how are you? You dona look so good."

Joe Maniscalco had lived in the United States for almost 30 years and spoke English as well as anyone on the street. But often he reverted to the accent of his native Sicily just for effect.

"Whatsa matter," he went on, "that you have to meet with your good friend from Italy? Ees it a job you want? You know I've been trying to get you to work for me for years. Ees it my friend Alex? Maybe he's not paying you enough?"

"Knock it off, Joe," Scorp said, forcing a smile. If I'd wanted the Mafia, I would have called Lennie, not you."

"So maybe my brother and I can do the job together, no?" Then, noticing the concern on Scorp's face, Joe laughed and pushed his plate aside. "OK, what's bugging you? You look like your wife ran away with your best friend or something. Come on, out with it."

"What do you know about Clark Hanson?" Scorp asked bluntly. I understand he worked for you once."

"So?" Joe said cautiously.

"You let him go, right? Why?"

"Why are you interested? And how do you know he worked for me?"

"I checked his personnel file," Scorp answered.

"What's it to you?" Joe asked, poking at the spaghetti on his plate. "Does Alex have you doing the hiring and firing these days?"

"Nope, just curious for my own reasons, off the record. You going to help me or not?"

"What do you want to know?"

"Why you let him go."

"This is off the record?"

"Yeah, that's what I said. Now what gives?" Scorp spoke in an urgent whisper.

"The guy wanted every Saturday off."

"That's it?"

"That's it."

Puzzled, Scorp demanded, "So why all the secrecy?"

"Regulations," Joe explained. "You're guaranteed certain religious rights in this country. An employer's got to make a reasonable attempt to accommodate an employee's sincerely held religious beliefs."

"And what if you don't?"

"If it came out that we fired him for wanting a day off to worship, we'd be fined or sued. Maybe both." Joe shrugged and added, "Clark's a good draftsman. Hated to let him go, but you know Gilotti. He may be my silent partner, but he's pretty vocal. He doesn't make exceptions, and I can't do much about it until I buy him out."

"So how'd you get away with it?" Scorp leaned forward.

"You mean firing him?" Joe asked. "Listen, I don't want to cause him any trouble."

"Come on, Joe. It's important."

"He was on probation," Joe shrugged. "As long as an employee is in a trial period, you don't have to give much reason for firing, unless that employee's a union member. Satisfied?"

"Yeah," Scorp smiled for the first time that night. "Yeah, I am. Thanks, Joe. Gotta run now, but I'll catch you around."

❧

"Got a minute?"

Alex turned from his desk as Scorp Johnson quietly shut the office door. "What's up?" he asked the sober engineer.

Scorp took a deep breath. "You need to know that Clark's causing problems with your employees. They think you're giving him preferential treatment. You guys eat lunch together, he gets Saturdays off, that kind of thing."

"He makes up the hours on Sundays," Alex reminded him.

"But we've always been a tight-knit group here, and now there's a lot of discontent. After I talked to everyone in the office, they agreed that things just aren't right. So I wrote up this letter," Scorp said, handing Alex several pages. "Most of the employees signed it. We, uh, just want to express our concerns and ask that you consider letting Clark Hanson go."

Confused, Alex stared at the signatures. "Have there been any problems with Clark's work?" he asked.

"Well, not yet, that I know of."

"Maybe it's just coincidence," Alex went on, "but yesterday I got a letter from Bill Eckroth. He said he's never had a better set of drawings than the last bunch we sent him. Who drew them, anyway?"

"Uh, Clark, I guess."

"I thought so. He also writes how much he's appreciated Clark's help. I understand he went to Bill's office and spent an hour with him making sure we knew exactly what he wanted. If Bill is singing his praises, what more can I ask, Scorp?"

"That's the problem," Scorp answered. "He's being singled out as something special. How about the rest of us?"

"Scorp," Alex said quietly, "it sounds to me like you've got a healthy case of jealousy."

Scorp scowled.

"Maybe I'm wrong, but I think there's another issue buried here. What's really eating at you, Scorp?"

Scorp didn't answer for a long time; he just looked down at his cowboy boots. Finally, he stared straight into Alex's eyes.

"He's a religious fanatic, Al."

"Hold on," Alex warned. "You know this is a free country."

Scorp launched his attack. "People like Clark are divisive. They create doubts for sincere Christians. They undermine confidence in pastors and churches."

By now Scorp was pacing furiously. He picked up the orange nerf ball on Alex's desk and began drilling it repeatedly at the small plastic basketball hoop mounted on the office wall.

He went on: "The Christian church has worshiped on the Lord's day since Jesus walked the earth. Jesus is the one who changed the day of worship. I don't want you and Melanie sucked into something that destroys the beauty of the gospel."

Scorp flattened the orange ball in his hands. "And consider this," he added. "What if Clark gets the whole office believing the same way he does? Who's going to do the work?"

The nerf ball sailed toward the hoop again, but Alex intercepted it. "Scorp," he said, "I want you to clarify something for me. Am I wrong, or did Jesus give the Sabbath at Creation?"

"Yes," Scorp answered slowly, "He was the Creator, but He—"

"Just a minute," Alex went on. "Does the Bible say it was God the Son who reminded Israel of His law, including the Sabbath, at Mount Sinai?"

"Yes, I guess so."

"Tell me, why would the Creator put people in bondage? That goes contrary to everything the Bible says about God. You're telling me that

Jesus came to free us from a law that He Himself gave us. Is that logical?"

Alex popped the nerf ball from his hands and reached for his Bible again. "Scorp," he said kindly, "I'm not trying to irritate you, but I'm not sure you're being fair with Clark. I'm really excited about some of the things he's introduced me to."

Scorp stopped pacing. "What did Jesus come to free us from if not the law?"

"Sin!" Alex declared, opening his Bible. "Romans 6 says He came to free us from slavery to sin, not from the law itself.

"Another thing," Alex added. "I've always wondered why Jesus had to die. If God could have done away with the law, why didn't He do it before Jesus died? Did God want His Son to suffer needlessly? Is God a sadist?"

"Of course not," Scorp muttered.

"The Bible says that Jesus came to pay the price for our sins, right? According to 1 John 3:4, sin is lawlessness. Without the law, sin doesn't exist, and there would have been no reason for Jesus to die."

Scorp settled into a chair and fidgeted.

"Alex," he interrupted, "you're really getting sucked into this, aren't you? You're a Sunday school teacher, and you can't see through this! Are you going to start preaching next?"

"Come on, Scorp," Alex pleaded. "That kind of sarcasm's beneath you." Standing up and opening the office door, he called, "Clark, can I see you for a minute?"

"Sure. Just let me save this file, and I'll be right in," Clark replied.

When Clark had seated himself beside Scorp, Alex closed the door and began. "Clark, Scorp has been with me since I opened this office. He's a trusted worker and my good fishing buddy. We've often prayed together, so when he expresses a concern, I listen carefully."

Alex sighed and looked at both men. "You both claim to be Christians," he continued, "which means you're supposed to love each other. People who care about each other should communicate. That's what we're going to do right now."

Scorp had been marshaling his forces for this confrontation ever since his lunch with Clark at Antonelli's. In order to impress Alex, he'd have to strike quickly, without appearing vindictive.

"Clark, I respect your convictions," Scorp began. "But you're dead wrong on this issue. I hope you won't take it personally."

Clark shook his head. "No, I understand," he said.

Scorp asked both men to turn to Matthew 5. "The life and teachings of Jesus contain the clearest picture of why He came to earth," he said. "Only He can make this issue crystal clear. Clark, you admit we're not saved by keeping the law, but you still believe we have to obey it. Talk's cheap, Clark. A Yankee by any other name is still a guy that wandered down from the North somewhere.

"Even though you say you're saved by Jesus' blood, you still seem to believe in being saved by your works. There's no gettin' around it: no matter how you dress the hog, it still says 'oink.'"

"Scorp!" Clark threw up his hands.

"Hold on, Clark. You'll get to say your piece in a minute. It's my turn."

Clark nodded and leaned back.

Scorp turned to Exodus. "Smack dead center in the middle of the Ten Commandments sits the Sabbath law," he said. "This law was given to Jews, not Christians. Look back in Matthew 5:17. Jesus says that he came to fulfill the law, right? Let's say I fulfill a promise to Alex. It's completed. Done with. And it's no longer an issue. Jesus died on the cross, and now the Ten Commandments, with the Sabbath at their center, are done with."

"What do you mean when you say 'done with'?" Clark asked.

"I mean they're extinct," Scorp fired back. "Like a dinosaur, they're interesting to look at but no longer relevant to anything."

"OK, Clark, it's your turn," Alex said.

"First, I want to say that this is not an issue of Jews or Gentiles. The world has seen many sincere, godly Jews. Abraham was one, and so was Paul."

"And so was Jesus," Alex murmured.

"It's not fair to throw the blanket of condemnation over all the Jews for killing Jesus," Clark went on. "Some Jewish people at a particular point in history asked for Jesus to die on the cross. Some Gentiles passed the sentence and pounded in the nails. We all bear the responsibility for Jesus' death."

Alex nodded and said, "So it's really not our heritage but our sins that put Him there."

"That's right," Clark agreed. "The Sabbath has nothing to do with Judaism, other than the fact that Jews have obeyed God and kept the Sabbath for thousands of years. Now, let's look at Matthew 5:17 again. Scorp, could you read it, please?"

"Sure. 'Think not that I have come to abolish the law and the prophets; I have come not to abolish them but to fulfil them'" (RSV).

"As far as I'm concerned," Clark explained, "to abolish something means to do away with it. Jesus uses the word twice, then contrasts it with *fulfill,* which must mean something totally different. Let's experiment and insert the phrase *do away with* in place of *fulfill.*" The men bent over their Bibles and followed silently as Clark read, "Think not that I have come to do away with the law and the prophets; I have come not to do away with them but to do away with them.'"

Alex smiled. "Doesn't compute, does it?" he said.

"*Strong's Concordance* helped me understand the contrast in this verse," Clark told them. "The word *fulfill,* as Jesus uses it here, means to fill full and make complete. Jesus came to fill the law of God with meaning, not to destroy it. He came to complete it. When I complete a project, I haven't destroyed it; instead, I've made it as perfect as I can."

Scorp frowned. "But why would Jesus need to fill His own law with meaning? It pretty much speaks for itself, doesn't it?"

"But for many folks in Jesus' time, keeping the law had degenerated into following the letter but forgetting the spirit," Clark reminded him. "Jesus came to show us that true loyalty and obedience are a matter of the heart. A heart that's right reveals itself in a person's actions.

"Jesus underscores this idea in Matthew 5:19 by saying that 'anyone who breaks one of the least of these commandments and teaches others to do the same will be called least in the kingdom of heaven, but whoever practices and teaches these commands will be called great in the kingdom of heaven' [NIV]. Then He tells His followers that their righteousness must exceed that of the Pharisees. These religious leaders kept the letter of the law, but not its spirit."

Taking a deep breath, Clark stopped. "One more thing before I'm done," he faltered. "I want to apologize. I'm sorry if I just sounded combative. It would break God's heart to see His people battling over a gift He had given them. Alex is right; we're both Christians, and I really hope we can be friends."

An uncomfortable silence followed. Scorp seemed to know his advantage had slipped away.

"Just one text," Scorp finally said. "If you can show me just one text that says Jesus or the New Testament writers expected us to keep the Sabbath, then I'll concede you're right. But we all know that the text isn't there, don't we?"

Alex answered this time. "Silence isn't a convincing argument, Scorp. Silence can mean that something is so clear that it doesn't need to be restated. It seems to me that the burden of proof lies with you. Unless you can show clearly that the day of worship was changed, then it's safe to assume the Sabbath is still in effect."

"Actually," Clark added, "the Sabbath is mentioned at least twice as applying to New Testament Christians."

Surprised, Scorp's face darkened again, and he folded his arms across his chest. Turning to Matthew 24:20, Clark explained that in those verses, Jesus spoke to His disciples about what His believers would face in the future, when the Roman armies would surround Jerusalem and they would have the opportunity to flee. 'Pray ye that your flight not be in the winter, neither on the sabbath day,'" he read. Then he added, "Either Jesus didn't know that He was about to change the day of worship, or else He believed that His disciples would still be keeping the Sabbath almost 40 years after His resurrection when the city was destroyed.

"Sabbath is mentioned again in the third and fourth chapters of Hebrews," Clark said, "where the seventh-day Sabbath is used as a symbol of the rest that God wants to give those who believe in Him. In this passage the writer argues that, even though Old Testament Israel failed to obtain that rest because they were disobedient and lacked faith, yet God still offers rest to His people today. I'm reading verses 9 through 11: 'There remains, then, a Sabbath-rest for the people of God; for anyone who enters God's rest also rests from his own work, just as God did from his. Let us, therefore, make every effort to enter that rest, so that none will fall by following their example of disobedience.'"

"What do you think, Scorp?" Alex asked. "You said that one verse would convince you, and it sounds like you've got a verse and nearly another whole chapter!"

Scorp's last words were forced. "Alex," he said, "I didn't come in here to be embarrassed and humiliated by you or Clark. I think he's wrong."

Storming from the office, he left Clark and Alex to face each other awkwardly.

Finally Alex spoke. "Clark, I guess I need some time to think."

CHAPTER 10

M r. Hammond, you've got to get here quick!"

Struggling to pull himself back to reality, Bob Hammond listened to the frantic voice on his phone. He had been dreaming that he lived in an apartment underneath a bowling alley. Now, rubbing the sleep from his eyes, he discovered the inspiration for his nightmare. The wind outside beat against his house like a hurricane. He flinched as thunder exploded overhead.

Bob recognized the panicked voice of Sherie, the night house supervisor at the nursing home he owned.

"What time is it?" he asked her.

"It's 4:30 in the morning, Mr. Hammond. The storm blew most of the roof off the older section. The new wing is leaking too. Water's everywhere."

Her voice rushed on, describing the destruction. Bob interrupted her, "OK, OK, I get the picture. What about the patients?"

"I don't know, Mr. Hammond. I'm scared. The nurses are moving everyone into the dining room, but I don't know how long they'll be safe there."

Bob jumped from his bed and headed toward his closet with the portable phone. "You're doing fine, Sherie," he assured. Jerking a shirt from its hanger, he tried to dress while holding the phone in one hand. "Get the maintenance guys and the whole day crew down there right away. Call Dr. Metzger so he can come over and check out the patients. Oh, and call Med-Trans to see when they can start moving people."

"Moving them where?"

"I don't know yet. I'll call the other facilities in town to see who has openings for the worst patients. Everyone else we'll have to send home, or somewhere. Until we get things fixed, that is."

Bob finished his instructions, slammed down the phone, and flicked on his bedside radio to the local news station. Pulling on a pair of jeans, he moaned, "I can't believe this happened now, just when the new wing has opened."

Bob had purchased Riverside Manor four years before. The previous owners had postponed maintenance and allowed the old mansion to deteriorate. Bob's friends shook their heads and said nothing could be done, but he set to work anyway. He replaced the roof, renovated the inside, redecorated the rooms, and improved the administrative and nursing practices. Once again, Riverside looked like a palace. But one Georgia storm had turned his dream to shambles.

"Oh, well," he sighed, pulling on his shoes. "I rebuilt it once, so I can do it again." His main concern now was for his patients. Digging his rain jacket out of the closet and jamming a cap on his head, he opened the door and ran for his car.

Later that morning, after two hours of grueling work, Bob wondered if he'd ever have the energy to rebuild.

"Mr. Hammond?" a man's voice said behind him.

"Yes?"

"Do you have a minute?"

Bob didn't even turn from where he crouched on the floor trying to remove the filter from an old shop vacuum. "If you're looking for a relative, you'll need to check with the office," he answered. "I'm not trying to be rude, but I've got my hands full."

"No, we're here to help," the man continued. "Norman Gregg, from the family services office, is my next-door neighbor. He said you guys probably needed volunteers to take care of everyone. Here we are."

Bob turned to see two couples wrapped in wet raincoats. "I'm Mike Silver," the man said. "This is my wife, Charlene, my friend Deion Maxwell, and his wife, Rio. About six or eight more helpers are waiting in the hall."

"Whew," Bob sighed in relief. "Yeah, we can use you for sure." He sent several volunteers down the hall to help the maintenance crew with emergency water pipe repairs. The others followed him to the dining room where the patients waited in wheelchairs and beds.

"How about your neighborhood?" Bob asked Rio as she removed her raincoat and laid it on a table. "Did you get hit hard too?"

"Not really," she replied, "but the weather service said there were tornadoes in some places. I heard that the old neighborhood just across Ross Creek got it pretty bad."

Bob sighed again. Some of his patients came from that area of town, and he knew they wouldn't be able to go home.

Rio noticed his concern. "What will happen to your patients?" she asked. "Could we take some of them to our homes?"

"Some, maybe," Bob paused as he turned to leave the dining room. "But most of them would be too hard for you to take care of yourself. And some of them are insisting on their own homes. They're frightened and confused, and home means safety to them."

Rio nodded as she gazed over the crowded room. "They definitely can't stay here," she declared.

"I know, I know," Bob agreed. "The health inspector was just here. She said they all needed to be out by this evening." Deep in thought, he turned down the hall, leaving Rio and the other volunteers to help the tired nurses.

❧

Within the next hour most of the patients were sent home or transferred to the hospital. Rio stretched her tired back as she listened to the moans and confused cries of the remaining men and women. She shuddered.

"Pitiful, isn't it?" her husband, Deion, spoke from behind her.

She nodded quietly. "Where will they put everyone?"

"Oh, they'll find places," he said, wrapping his arms around his wife. "Bob Hammond was just telling me about a sweet little Polish man that's been begging for his wife all morning. The poor guy wants to go home, but his wife lives in that neighborhood that got hit so hard. I guess Norman Gregg got a call from her this morning, and most of her roof's blown off. She's been out borrowing buckets and pans to catch the water, but her house is still like a swimming pool."

Rio bit her lip for a minute, and then she spoke timidly. "Deion, we could help."

"How?" Deion asked, sneaking a look at his watch. "The Georgia game starts in three hours. We've got to hit the road now, or we'll be stuck in traffic all morning."

"Deion! These people need us now. We need to go over and get her house ready for her husband to come home."

Rio grew excited. "I know Mike would help," she added. "He's been telling us all about helping people on Saturday, or Sabbath, I guess he calls it. This is a good chance to see what it's like. It's what Jesus would have done, Deion. We both know that."

Deion groaned. "Rio, I haven't missed the Georgia game since college. It's bad enough that Mike's not going this year, but for me to miss the game . . . come on . . . you're asking too much, baby."

Rio folded her arms. "OK, we'll go to the game. But first I want you to meet someone."

Leading him to a dim corner, Rio bent and gently touched the shoulder of a gray-haired gentleman in faded blue overalls. His head faced the window.

"Mr. Kowalski," she called into his ear, "I want you to meet my husband."

"Come on, Rio, this isn't fair," Deion started to turn, then stopped as the old man's faded eyes turned toward the sound of his voice. Tears ran down his pink cheeks, leaving blotches on his flannel shirt.

"This is my husband, Deion," Rio said clearly. "And Deion, this is Mr. Kowalski."

"Pleased to meet you," the older man said. "Your wife is so kind."

He's blind, Deion realized. *Blind and alone.*

"I have to see my Helena," the man said. "For 70 years I took care of her, and now she needs me at home. Always she thinks she can take care of herself. She's a sweet one, my Helena. Tiny, but so strong. Like dynamite, her papa always said." Rocking in his chair, Mr. Kowalski turned his head back toward the window.

"We don't even know where he lives, Rio," Deion whispered. "How do you know he has a wife?" He'd heard about how old people get out of touch with reality. Maybe the man's wife was dead or living with other relatives. Maybe he'd never had a wife. Who could know?

Rio hissed back at him, "Deion! You're the one who told me about his wife. And now she's floating around in her own house. You guys could make it watertight for now. Come on."

"I don't know where she lives."

She grinned. "Mr. Hammond does. And so does Norman Gregg. Ask them."

"I don't want to." He knew he had to see that football game.

"Pray about it, Deion."

Deion's voice rose, and he paced tensely. "Pray? What's there to pray about?"

"Deion, you're the one who's always telling me to pray about things." Rio waited as her husband nervously folded and unfolded a metal chair.

"Rio, I don't need you telling me when to pray. I'll pray when I want, and I won't when I don't. God doesn't want us to miss that game for some little old . . ." Deion glanced over at Mr. Kowalski. "Some old . . ."

"Please, Deion," Rio begged quietly.

"All right, I'll pray about it," he sputtered and pivoted toward the door. "I'll pray, but while I do that, you get the kids ready. We're going to that football game."

CHAPTER 11

"Mrs. Kowalski?"

"Who's asking?" A small white-haired woman peered through the bars of her security door at the small crowd on her porch.

"I'm Mike Silver, and these—"

"Huh?" the tiny woman yelled. "I don't hear so good. Now get out of here, or I'll call the police!"

Glancing at the quiet neighborhood, Mike hoped he wasn't waking up anyone trying to sleep late on a Saturday morning. *Oh well*, he thought, as several curtains moved and faces appeared in the windows of nearby houses, *at this age, they're all early risers anyway.*

Turning back to the front door of the powder-blue cottage, he looked down at the belligerent woman facing him through the door.

"Mrs. Kowalski," he shouted, "Norman Gregg sent us."

"I don't know no Norma Gray. Why are you bothering me?"

"Norman Gregg," Mike repeated. "Norman Gregg from family services."

"So why didn't you say so?" Helen Kowalski shouted, reaching a shaky hand toward the latch. What does Norman Gregg want? And who are you, anyway? Going around scaring an old lady like that. You should be ashamed of yourselves!"

"Mrs. Kowalski, my name is Mike Silver, and these are some of my friends," Mike pointed to the group behind him.

"So, what is this, a convention or something? My yard is full of people. Why are you here?"

It should be obvious, Mike thought, looking up at the destroyed roof.

Deion whispered quietly behind him. "When that old wind quit blowing last night, this place must've been like a sieve. There aren't enough pots and pans in the whole neighborhood to catch all the water from those holes."

Trying not to smile, Mike shouted again, "Mrs. Kowalski, Norman Gregg said you needed some help. He said your roof was leaking because of the storm."

She started to close her door again. "Since when is an old lady's leaking roof any of your business?"

"Mrs. Kowalski, we're here to help. The storm damaged Riverside Manor, and all the patients have to leave today. Your husband wants to be with you, so they're bringing him home at 8:00 tonight."

"We can take care of ourselves, young man!"

"But Mrs. Kowalski, Norman told us that you're alone. Don't you want the house to be ready for your husband? You can't let him come home to a house that's leaking water everywhere. We'll throw some plastic over the roof for now, and later we'll come back to fix it."

"That roof is not fixable," she declared.

"Then we'll replace it," Mike told her. "But for now, we just want to make you comfortable."

"Get out of here," she ordered. "I can't pay for all this. What's with that Norman Gregg—sending a mob over here when he knows I can't pay." She shouted firmly at first, but then her voice shook as she retreated into her dripping home.

"It's already been paid for," Mike said.

"I don't take charity!"

"It's not charity," he insisted. "It's a gift from someone who cares about you."

"Cares about me? Nobody cares about me," she said. She shook her finger at Mike's face. "And a gift? I don't know anybody who'd give me a present. Is this one of those scams? I've heard of these things, you know."

Mike pulled out a white card and handed it to her. "Mrs. Kowalski, here's Norman Gregg's home number. Call and ask him."

"Young man, don't tell me who to call. I can decide these things for myself."

"So, can we help you, Mrs. Kowalski?" They all waited in silence.

She thought carefully and then nodded. "Just this once," she agreed. "But no funny business. And keep those kids out of my rosebushes."

Mike grinned triumphantly. "Great. Now let me introduce everyone. Gesturing to a middle-aged couple standing on the walk, he said, "This is Darin and Beverly Mancovicz."

"You're Polish?"

"Yes, Mrs. Kowalski," Darin stepped forward and extended his hand. "My father's from Gdansk."

She nodded approvingly. Mike introduced Charlene, Rio, Deion, their kids, and the other friends who'd come to help.

"How come you're not watching that big football game?" she asked them.

Rio smiled as Deion stepped forward to answer. "We just think this is more important." It was almost dark when the families finished their work and reclined on the lawn to enjoy the retreating colors of a north Georgia sunset.

"Well, we did it," Mike sighed, looking up as a flash of lightning lit up a distant thundercloud. The next storm was moving in ahead of schedule.

Deion settled on the wet grass beside him. "You know, we've really got to do something about that bathroom door when we come back to fix the roof," Mike said. "It's way too narrow for a wheelchair. And we need to rig up a wheelchair ramp if Mr. K is going to be here very long."

Deion laughed and added, "You know, Mike, I thought you and Rio were nuts at first, but this has been great. The kids loved it too."

"So, you're sitting around on the job, are you?" Mrs. Kowalski said, sticking her frizzy white head out the door. In the Old Country—"

"Mrs. Kowalski, we're finished," Charlene interrupted. "Everything's ready for your husband."

"That I can see with my own eyes," the little

lady said, a smile breaking out on her face for the first time since they had arrived. "And a good job you did. I know these things. My Arthur was a good worker too. The best."

Reaching behind her, she brought out a huge platter of chocolate-chip cookies and a plastic jug of milk. "Now you are hungry, I think," she told them. "Probably you're going out to eat pizza, yes? Those Italians! Nothing but cheese and tomato sauce. It's no good for you." She clucked her tongue, shook her head, and held the cookies out for the workers.

"Now, make sure the little ones get their share," she added. "They worked hard and didn't step on my roses one time. I was watching."

As the group munched on their cookies, Mrs. Kowalski beckoned to Deion. "You're the leader here, no?" she asked him. "How much do I owe you? I'm a poor woman, but I can borrow money. Tell me the truth."

"No charge," Deion said kindly as he got up and walked over to the little lady. "It's a gift, remember?"

"Who do I know that would give me a gift like this?"

"Mrs. Kowalski, this is a special day. Do you know what today is?" Deion asked, glancing over at Mike for encouragement.

"Of course, it's Saturday," she sputtered. "I'm old, but I still know things, young man."

"Yes, but it's more than that, Mrs. K. It's called the Sabbath. It's God's special gift to you.

He likes to spend the day with the people who love Him, and today He led us over here to help you. We just get to be His hands and feet."

Mrs. Kowalski tilted her head. "And He's not going to send me a bill?"

"No, never," Deion told her. "Jesus paid the price 2,000 years ago when He died on the cross. We're just now getting around to delivering your gift. Can you understand?"

"I'm not sure that I do," she replied.

"Let me try to explain it another way. When God made this world, He gave us the Sabbath. It's a day for worship and being with each other and helping folks who need us. The finest worship we can give Him is to feed the hungry, clothe the naked, shelter those who need it, and minister to the sick. That's why we're here—because God loves you, and so do we."

With that, Deion bent and gave the speechless lady a little kiss on her forehead. "Now, go on inside, honey," he said softly. "It's been a long day, and Mr. Kowalski will be home soon."

She stuffed their pockets full of extra cookies and waved as the crew piled into cars and drove away in the twilight.

For a long time old Mrs. Kowalski stood in the doorway, the lamplight silhouetting her tiny frame, the security door open at night for the first time in years. Reaching up and touching the spot where Deion had kissed her, she gazed out at the street and wept.

CHAPTER 12

Alex, you have a call on line 3."

Jackie's voice on the intercom cut through Alex's daydreaming. A week had passed since his talk with Scorp and Clark, and he and Melanie hadn't done much sleeping since. Instead, they sat up every night studying and restudying what the Bible said about the Sabbath.

"Who is it, Jackie?"

"I didn't ask his name, Alex. He said it was personal."

Picking up the phone, he said, "This is Alex."

"Hi, my name is Ryan Goodbrad," a man answered. "I'm the pastor of Saint Ignatius Catholic Church here in town. I'm also in a study group with a couple of your friends. They said I might be able to answer some questions for you."

Alex drew a blank for a second. Then he remembered. "Oh, yeah, about how the Sabbath was changed to Sunday."

"That's right," Ryan said. "I did some graduate work on the subject."

"Sure, I'd love to talk with you," Alex said, reaching for his appointment book. "Forgive me, but I'm not sure what to call you. Father? Pastor?"

"Why don't you just call me Ryan?"

"Fine, Ryan. Listen, my wife would love to sit in on this conversation. Could you come over for supper, say, on Thursday night?"

"I'd love it," Ryan replied. "Mike Silver says the cooking at your house is spectacular. My housekeeper moved, so I've been on my own for a week. One subject they skipped in seminary was gourmet cooking for parish priests. Peanut butter sandwiches and tomato juice are getting old."

Alex laughed. "We'll kill the fatted calf for you. How's 6:00 sound? Our address is 2604 Brightenbush Lane."

"Sounds good to me. See you then."

❧

"Whoa!" Ryan exclaimed when he sat down at the table with Alex's family on Thursday night. "My salivary glands are working overtime just thinking about all this good food."

"I hope you like lamb," Melanie said. "Rack of lamb is my favorite, and Alex likes pilaf and tabbouleh, which is an Arabic salad. The kids love pita bread, so I guess you'll be eating Middle Eastern tonight. Oh, and I made Italian cream cake for dessert."

"And I helped decorate it," Denae added proudly.

After the blessing, Ryan turned to Alex and said, "Mike and Francis tell me you've been doing some pretty intensive study lately."

"That's an understatement!" Alex answered. "We're excited about what we've found, but some pieces are still missing from the puzzle."

"Like what?"

Ryan helped himself to the food as Melanie

explained. "In all our study, from Genesis to Revelation, we've found only one day that God made holy, and that's the seventh-day Sabbath. Yet virtually the whole Christian world worships on Sunday." She paused to hand Denae the butter plate. "How on earth did the day change? And when?"

"There's another question," Alex interjected. "Why do so many people get hostile when you bring up the subject? I've asked a few people what they think about the Sabbath, and boy, you can see the hair start to rise on the backs of their necks. It was like I had tossed them a snake or something. If the day changed for a good reason, why do people have such strong emotions about it?"

"Well, let's start with the easier question," Ryan answered. "In seminary I wrote a paper on the change from Sabbath to Sunday, so I'm familiar with the story.

"As you know, the Christian church grew out of Judaism. The best evidence available shows that Christians were initially Sabbath-keepers. We have no historical evidence indicating that the day of worship changed in the first century after Jesus died."

Melanie looked perplexed. "Then why has everyone been trying to show us that Jesus changed the day?"

Ryan held up his hand. "Wait, we'll get to that later," he said. "Many historians do believe that early Christians began to celebrate Jesus' resurrection on Sunday. But it was just a holiday, like Thanksgiving or the Fourth of July today. It didn't replace the Sabbath."

"Meanwhile, in the Roman Empire, things were pretty tough for the Jews. They had a nasty habit of rebelling against Rome. That's why the Romans. got fed up and finally destroyed Jerusalem in A.D. 70. I can understand the Jewish sentiment; no one likes to be ruled by another nation, especially when you believe you have a divine destiny to lead the world. And I can also understand the Roman reaction. Anti-Jewish feelings grew so strong that no one wanted to be associated with the Jews.

"At the same time, the Christians had their own problems. Nero, looking for a scapegoat after he burned Rome, blamed them. Hadrian also hated Christians and tried to wipe them out. He even outlawed worship on the Sabbath. Anyone who disobeyed made a quick trip to the Colosseum as dinner for the lions."

Denae and Little Al stared at their food and then at each other in horror.

Ryan continued his story. "Now, remember that Jesus was a Jew. And Paul was a Jew. Worse yet, the Christians worshiped on a day associated with Judaism."

"Sounds like they were under double jeopardy," Alex commented. "They were hated for following Christ and for keeping the same Sabbath as the Jews."

"Exactly," Ryan agreed. "And that's why it's

no wonder that some began to drift away from keeping the Sabbath. Cultural issues affected them too. Many prominent Romans worshiped the sun, so the day of Sunday became more important. By about A.D. 200 we begin to find references in early church histories that some Christians kept Sunday as their day of worship. Since Sabbath was such a liability, it was easy to begin rationalizing the change."

Ryan glanced around the table. "Am I going into too much detail?" he asked.

"Not at all," Melanie said. "I'm just afraid you're not getting a chance to eat."

"Oh, I'm doing all right," Ryan answered. "But could I have a little more of the lamb, please? It's delicious!"

After adding another helping of rice and a serving of tabbouleh to his plate, Ryan continued. "The real change in the day of worship occurred about 150 years later. By then Christianity had made serious inroads in the Roman Empire. In fact, we have a letter from a Roman governor complaining that the Christians were everywhere—in the army, in the markets, in the courts, and even in the emperor's household.

"By the time Constantine became the emperor, Sunday had replaced Sabbath in the minds of many Christians. He went one step further and issued an edict ordering all judges, city people, and artisans to rest on the venerable day of the sun. That gave Sunday even more status."

"Are you serious about all this?" Alex cocked his head to one side, an amazed look on his face.

"Dead serious! None of this is new if you're a Catholic. Only you Protestants have a problem with all the history you're hearing. It's the source of your greatest inconsistency."

"How's that?" Melanie asked as she began slicing the cake.

"Well, Protestants started out by protesting," Ryan explained. "Early Protestants fought against many teachings and practices of the Roman Catholic Church. Martin Luther and the other Reformers continually challenged Rome, especially when it elevated tradition over what the Bible taught."

"They didn't believe people should be worshiping Mary and the other saints, right?" Alex asked.

"Yes, and that's not all. For example, some Protestants disagreed with infant baptism. Some didn't believe that the Communion bread and wine actually become the body and blood of Christ in the Eucharist. And no Protestant would even begin to agree with the infallibility of the pope as he spoke from his chair in Saint Peter's Cathedral. But almost nobody protested about one key issue. It's always puzzled me."

"May I interrupt you long enough to ask if you'd like coffee with your cake?" Melanie asked.

"Do you have decaf?"

"Sure, that's about all we drink around

here," she answered.

"Then I'll have some."

"Now, go on," Alex urged. "This is fascinating."

"Well, for centuries the Catholic Church has claimed responsibility for changing the day of worship from the Sabbath to Sunday. In many Roman Catholic sources, the change is given as a proof that the pope has the power to change even the law of God."

"Are you saying that Catholics believe God's law was done away with by the pope?" Alex asked.

"Actually, no. Only some Protestants think God's law was abolished. Catholics believe the pope was given the power of God to change the law. For the life of me, I can't figure out why so many Protestants accept that change. They're actually agreeing with the pope's power to represent God on earth.

"Let's take it one step further. The Roman Catholic Church still considers Protestant churches an estranged part of the family. But the church also believes that they will one day return. Even now, the Catholic Church is dominant in the religious world. The greatest proof of that is that Protestants worship on Sunday, a day that the Catholic Church set aside as holy."

"Where could I read that in a Catholic source?" Alex asked.

"Oh, there's a number of them. For instance,

the old *Convert's Catechism of Catholic Doctrine* asks the question:

"'Which is the Sabbath day?'

"The answer is given: 'Saturday is the Sabbath day.'

"'Why do we observe Sunday instead of Saturday?' it goes on to ask.

"The answer is 'We observe Sunday instead of Saturday because the Catholic Church, in the Council of Laodicea (A.D. 336), transferred the solemnity from Saturday to Sunday.'"

Ryan refused a second helping of Melanie's cake before he continued with several more examples. "Bishop Keenan's *Doctrinal Catechism* says that Protestants substitute Sunday for Sabbath without scriptural authority. And James Cardinal Gibbons, in *The Faith of Our Fathers*, says that one cannot find a single line in the Bible authorizing Sunday worship.

"Protestants claim to make the Bible their first rule of faith," Ryan pointed out. "The rallying cry of the Reformation was *sola scriptura*, which in Latin means 'the Scripture alone.' Still they're willing to set aside the Bible Sabbath for a day that's purely Catholic in origin. Some even invent complicated defenses for it."

Alex and Melanie exchanged knowing looks. "We've heard enough of those to last a lifetime," Alex told Ryan.

"Now, remember something," Ryan continued. "I was raised to believe that church tradition and the proclamations of the pope are equal with the Bible. In fact, that they supersede it when the pope speaks officially from his throne in Saint Peter's Cathedral. Therefore, I have no problem accepting the change. If you believe as we do, our position on the Sabbath is very logical. If you don't, then it makes no sense at all."

"If that's true, why do so many Protestant pastors defend Sunday worship?" Alex asked.

"In many cases, it's just ignorance. They were taught certain ideas in church or in seminary, so they've always believed them," Ryan answered. "However, right now there's an amazing surge of interest in the subject, and many people, pastors included, are studying it all for themselves."

"I still don't understand why so many Protestants accept the change," Alex said. "Basically, they're accepting tradition over the Bible."

"I think it has a lot to do with human nature," Ryan replied. "When you believe and practice something all your life, it's hard to admit you've been wrong. Human pride is pretty powerful sometimes."

"Do any Protestant churches worship on the Sabbath?" Melanie asked.

"Yes, in fact, some of them are well-established denominations all around the world," Ryan told them. "And many individuals, like you two, are studying the matter independently."

"So what about you, Ryan?" Alex asked. "Where do you stand on this?"

"You mean personally?" Ryan smiled as he reached over and stroked Toots' ears. "As I said, the issue for me lies in a different place. I'm having to rethink whether I'm going to accept the Bible or the traditions of the church as the final authority in my life. I don't know if you can appreciate the implications of that, but for me, it's pretty scary. You've made a commitment to each other in marriage, right? Well, a Catholic priest makes that kind of commitment to the church and the pope.

"I've wanted to be a priest since I was 6 years old," he continued. "If I decided that the church and the Bible conflict with each other . . . and if I decided to renounce my loyalty to the church, I'd lose everything. It's not easy for me."

Ryan glanced at his watch and gave Toots another pat before he stood. "I'd better be going," he said. "The meal was a masterpiece. Thank you very much, both of you."

Melanie thanked him for the compliment and asked him to come again. As Ryan buttoned his coat, he sighed and looked at Alex and Melanie and their two children.

"You have some serious decisions to make," he told them. "It won't be easy. The devil makes sure that the really important decisions never are!"

CHAPTER 13

It was one of those bright spring days when people feel like singing at work. Five months had passed since Clark's first week at Bowen and Associates.

Even Scorp seems cheerful, Clark thought as he finished the drawings for a new hangar at the airport. He glanced out the window, wishing he could be out with the surveying crew. *Maybe I can get out later and do some site work in the sunshine,* he hoped. Saving his file, he sent it to the plotter so he'd have a copy for staff meeting.

Alex had called in all the survey crews and project supervisors. Even Melanie was at the office that day, arranging a feast of Antonelli's pizza and soft drinks for everyone. At noon the office filled with workers sitting on desks, chairs, and even the floor. After everyone had filled up on pizza and root beer, Alex made his way to the front.

"The past few months have been challenging for me and my family," Alex began. "As you know, Melanie and I are Christians. We've never tried to push our religion on you, but we have tried to run our business as we believe Jesus would if He were here on earth."

Melanie slipped in beside Alex, and he squeezed her hand. "We've also tried to remain open to God's leading in our lives," he added. "We're eternally grateful for His patience as He teaches us.

"Today I have some important matters to discuss with you. First, I'd like to apologize," Alex announced. His employees listened quietly.

He continued, "When I started this business, I vowed to make it the best engineering and surveying firm in the region. You've all helped me accomplish that, but I'm afraid I've been insensitive to you and the needs of your families.

"God created us to work hard. But He also designed us to need rest, recreation, and time with our families. In my pursuit of excellence, I've often left you with no time for these other important areas of life. I'm truly sorry."

The engineers, draftsmen, surveyors, and other workers exchanged surprised glances.

"Several months ago Melanie and I found out that God has given us some very special gifts," Alex said. "He's given us life and family and a special day of quality time. The Bible calls that day the Sabbath. It extends from sundown Friday night to sundown Saturday night.

"I'd like to share with you what God says about His special day. The invitation to keep the Sabbath is one of the Ten Commandments, right alongside 'Thou shalt not steal' and 'Thou shalt not kill' and all the others. It's found in the book of Exodus, chapter 20, verses 8 through 11, and here's how it reads:

" 'Remember the Sabbath day by keeping it holy. Six days you shall labor and do all your work, but the seventh day is a Sabbath to the Lord your God. On it you shall not do any work, neither you, nor your son or daughter, nor your manservant or maidservant, nor your animals, nor the alien within your gates. For in six days the Lord made the heavens and the earth, the sea, and all that is in them, but he rested on the seventh day. Therefore the Lord blessed the Sabbath day and made it holy.'

"Melanie and I studied all we could about the Sabbath in the Bible. We wanted to be sure about this, and now we are. We're setting that day aside for its intended purpose, which means that we'll spend the time with God and our family and friends."

"And we can't wait to begin!" Melanie interrupted with a smile.

The workers looked confused. "So you're not coming to work tomorrow?" one of the draftsmen asked.

"No," declared Alex, "and neither are you. Starting today, we'll be closing the office at 4:00 on Fridays. And no more Saturday catch-up days. If we can't get it done during the week, it'll have to wait!"

A few employees looked stunned, some started clapping, and soon everyone was cheering. No one seemed to hear Alex's last few announcements about training sessions and future projects.

"One more thing," he finished. "If anyone would like to know more about our Sabbath discovery, Melanie and I would love to share it with you."

The sun sank low in the Friday afternoon sky. *Only an hour until sundown,* Connie Hanson noted. She hummed to herself as she added a final touch of salt to a steaming pot of potato soup. Checking to make sure the garlic bread was ready, she thought about the past several months. She remembered how worried they'd been when Clark first started working for Alex. But now he loved his job and never had problems getting his Sabbaths off.

She also thought about the countless lunch conversations between Clark and Alex. She wondered if the Bowens would one day decide to keep God's Sabbath. *Guide them, Father,* she prayed, *and let them know how much You love spending time with them.*

Outside the kitchen window, a cheerful robin celebrated the warmth of a spring sunset. Connie rejoiced in the sense of God's presence that she always felt as Sabbath approached.

"Connie?"

She'd been so absorbed that she hadn't heard the door open. She whirled to greet her beaming husband.

"Connie," Clark said, "you'll never guess what happened at work today!"

Experience happiness no problem can take away!

When problems weigh you down, where do you turn? Millions of people have found the answer in a relationship with Jesus Christ.

Happiness Digest shows how you too can experience His joy and guidance, and offers help in the calm assurance that God is in ultimate control and very much interested in your life.

13 Life-changing Secrets

by Mark Finley speaker/director of
It Is Written **telecast ministry**

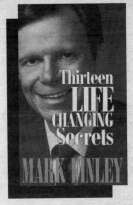

This powerful book is filled with stories that are really going to move you. Stories about people staggered by the blow of divorce, drug addiction, abuse, abandonment, death, and financial problems. People longing for something better. And finding it!

All these people responded to the touch of God. And when they did, something incredible happened. Their discoveries about who He *really* is flooded their lives with happiness.

As you share their experiences, you'll discover 13 secrets that can make an exciting difference in your life, too.

Paperback, 122 pages.
US$1.99, Cdn$2.70

Feel the Difference
Vibrant Life Makes

Vibrant Life lets you know how to feel your best. Get life-changing advice on nutrition and fitness. Discover simple ways to avoid disease. Enjoy wholesome, delicious recipes.

If you want to experience more strength, more energy, and more peace of mind, subscribe to *Vibrant Life*, the one health magazine that recognizes the connection between faith in God and your well-being.

Credit card orders: 1-800-456-3991.

❏ Please send me one year (six issues) of *Vibrant Life* for only US$9.97. I save 33 percent off the cover price of US$15.00.

Your Name _____

Address _____

City _____

State, Zip _____

Please add US$5.10 per subscription for addresses outside the U.S.A. as well as GST in Canada. Mail with check or money order to: *Vibrant Life*, P.O. Box 1119, Hagerstown, MD 21741.

651-02-0